REVISE EDEXCEL
FUNCTIONAL SKILLS LEVEL 2

Mathematics

REVISION GUIDE

Series Consultant: Harry Smith

Author: Sharon Bolger

To practise all the topics covered in this book, check out:

Revise Functional Skills Level 2
Mathematics Revision Workbook 9781292145648

THE REVISE SERIES
For the full range of Pearson revision titles, visit:
www.pearsonschools.co.uk/revise

Contents

1-to-1 page match with the Level 2 Revision Workbook
ISBN 978 129214 584 8

A small bit of small print
Edexcel publishes Sample Test Materials on its website. This is the official content and this book should be used in conjunction with it. The questions in *Now try this* have been written to help you practise every topic in the book. Remember: the real test questions may not look like this.

Online test preparation

If you are taking the online test, you will need to understand how it works. Before you start, read the instructions about how to use the test and make sure you know what all the icons do.

Useful icons

 You can click the Time icon to find out how much time you have left on your test. The time will appear in the bottom right-hand corner.

 The timer does not stop when you click on the help button. You will be reminded when you have 15 minutes left, and again when you have 5 minutes left in the test.

 You can click this Help icon if you want a demonstration of how the online test buttons work.

 If you are unsure how to answer a question, click the Flag icon and move on to the next question. Come back to the questions you have flagged later.

 Before you use the final 5 minutes to check your answers, go back to any questions you have **flagged**.

 When you click the Review icon, all your flagged questions will appear. To go back and answer one of the questions you have flagged, click on that line.

  These buttons move you from question to question.

 Be very careful with the Quit button. If you click on it and then click on 'Yes', you will not be able to return to the test even if you haven't finished!

See page 3 for useful tips on how to use the onscreen calculator.

Changing the test settings

Click on the + button in the bottom left-hand corner of the screen to open the settings box.

Use the colour and zoom reset buttons to go back to the original settings.

Click the arrows to move around the page when you are zoomed in.

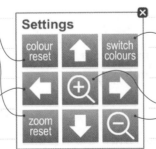

Click the switch colours icon to change the colour of the test to make it easier to read.

Click the magnifying glass icons to zoom in and out.

Now try this

1 How do you find out how much time is left?
2 What can you do if you can't read the test clearly?

Online test tools

If you are taking the online test, it is a good idea to prepare by practising using the online tools to answer questions.

 ## Show your working

When asked to show your working, write **every step** of your working out in the working out box. Type the numbers and click on the blue buttons to add in symbols.

When you have worked out the answer, you will need to show this by:

- clicking yes or no
- typing your answer in an answer box
- clicking a drop-down list and selecting the right option
- selecting the right answer from a list of options by putting a tick in the box.

You might get marks for working out even if your final answer is wrong.

 ## Tables

When you see a table, you could be asked to:

- click a particular row or column
- type information into an empty cell
- drag and drop data into a cell.

To drag and drop:

1 Click on the thing you want to move and drag it to where you want it.

2 Drop it into the empty space.

Playground	Story time	Drawing

	Session 1	Session 2	Session 3
Group A			
Group B			

 ## Shape and space

You could be asked to place an object onto a plan. This object represents a home cinema system.

 Click and drag the object to the floor plan. Drag the dots at the corners of the object to resize it.

 ## Graphs

You could be asked to display information as a graph. Remember to fill in all the missing information.

✓ Type in the graph title.

✓ Type in the axis labels and scales. The answer boxes will expand to fit the text you type in them.

✓ To plot each point, drag the cross to the graph and drop it in the right position. The red line connecting the points will appear automatically.

✓ Check your graph. You can move the points by clicking and dragging them.

Now try this

1 Why is it important to show your working out?

2 How can you prepare for your online test?

Using the onscreen calculator

You are allowed to use a calculator in your test. Make sure you know how to use one.
If you are doing the online test, press the blue button to open the onscreen calculator.

inserts brackets ————

stores a value in the memory ———

recalls a value from the memory ———

adds the number to the memory value

subtracts the number from the memory value

clears the last number entered

clears all calculations

For some questions, the onscreen calculator will be a scientific calculator. Make sure you know how to use the pi (π) button.

Order of operations

You will sometimes need to do calculations that involve more than one step.

You can enter each step separately or you can type in the whole calculation at once.

If you type in the whole calculation, make sure you use the correct order of operations. Use brackets where necessary.

Click 'Copy to working box' to show your working out.

If you are sitting a paper test, you will be allowed to use your own calculator. Make sure you are familiar with how to use it before the test.

Worked example

A nursery teacher buys a toy and a drink for four children. The toy costs 99p and the drink costs 45p.

Work out the total amount the teacher spends.

You need to be careful when using your calculator to do all the steps at once. Make sure you put brackets in the right place and always check your answer.

Method 1 – work out each step separately

Cost for a toy and drink for each child:

$99 + 45 = 144$p or £1.44

Total cost for four children:

$4 \times £1.44 = £5.76$

Method 2 – use a calculator to do all the steps at once

$(99 + 45) \times 4 = £5.76$

Now try this

For these questions, use your calculator. Write down the buttons you press to do the calculation both in individual steps and all at once.

A carpenter needs to make three tables. The wood for each table costs £26 and the fixings cost £2.

(a) How much will all the tables cost to make?

(b) The carpenter sells each table for £50. How much money does he make?

Number and place value

It is important to know the size of the numbers you see around you. The position of the digits tells you their value. A quick way to read numbers is to group them in threes from the right-hand side.

Worked example

1 (a) Write the number 7406 in words.

seven thousand, four hundred and six

(b) Write the number 342 568 in words.

three hundred and forty-two thousand, five hundred and sixty-eight

(c) Write the number thirty-four million, six hundred thousand, eight hundred and twenty-three in figures.

34 600 823

	tens of millions	millions	hundred thousands	ten thousands	thousands	hundreds	tens	units
(a)					7	4	0	6
(b)			3	4	2	5	6	8
(c)	3	4	6	0	0	8	2	3

The zero means 'no tens'

300 000 or 3 hundred thousands

The zeros fill the empty spaces

Worked example

2 The manager of a company wants to order the amount each member of the sales team earned in one financial quarter.

£123,506   £38,004   £42,023   £42,830

Order these amounts from smallest to largest.

£38,004   £42,023   £42,830   £123,506

These are all whole numbers, so the number with the most digits has the highest value. Use the commas to work out the place value of each digit in the other numbers.

Now try this

1 (a) Write the number 43 003 204 in words.
   (b) Write the number sixty-two million, five hundred thousand in figures.
2 Write the value of the 4 in each of these numbers.
   (a) 2432   **(b)** 42321   **(c)** 43 231 037
3 A television broadcaster wants to analyse how many people watched a programme each week. Order these viewing figures from largest to smallest.

week A:	week B:	week C:	week D:
1 452 034	1 425 043	1 402 043	1 502 453

Negative numbers

Numbers that are greater than zero are called positive numbers. Numbers that are lower than zero are called negative numbers. You need to be able to use negative numbers in lots of different situations and questions.

Number line

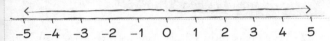

A number line can help you write numbers in order of size.

As you go to the **left** the numbers get **lower**.

As you go to the **right** the numbers get **higher**.

O is neither positive nor negative.

Identifying negative numbers

A negative number has a negative (−) sign before it.

−2, −4, −6 are all negative numbers.

A positive number sometimes has a positive (+) sign before it.

+3, +7, +9 are all positive numbers.

A number that doesn't have a sign before it is always positive.

4, 8, 10 are all positive numbers.

Worked example

1 Here are the average temperatures in different areas of Alaska:

Anchorage −1 °C   Seward 2 °C   Gulkana −8 °C

Homer 0 °C   Talkeetna −3 °C   Valdez 1 °C

What is the difference between the coldest and warmest temperatures?

$2 − −8 = 10$

The difference is 10°C

> Subtract the coldest temperature from the warmest temperature. Count from 2 to O and then from O to −8

Worked example

2 This company balance sheet shows the balance at the end of each month for the first four months of the year.

(a) For how many months was the company overdrawn?

2 months (January and April)

Month	Balance
January	−£340
February	£8,100
March	£2,600
April	−£1,200

(b) In which month was the company most overdrawn?

April (−£1,200)

> When the company is overdrawn, the balance is negative.

Now try this

1 Write these numbers in order of size starting with the lowest number.

62, 13, −23, −72, 0, −63

2 The temperature of a freezer in a restaurant must be −18 °C or less. Which of these temperatures are less than −18 °C?

−22 °C, −11 °C , 14 °C, 5 °C, −12 °C

Adding and subtracting

You will need to be able to decide whether to add or subtract to answer different types of questions.

Worked example

1 A waiter has three customers.
The first customer leaves a tip of £8.32 and
the second customer leaves a tip of £13.34
The waiter earned £30.04 in tips in total.

   (a) How much did the third customer give
   the waiter in tips?

£8.32 + £13.34 = £21.66
£30.04 – £21.66 = £8.38

   (b) The waiter bought a drink and a
   sandwich using his tips. The drink cost
   £2.32 and the sandwich was £3.49
   How much did he have left?

£2.32 + £3.49 = £5.81
£30.04 – £5.81 = £24.23

You need to decide whether to add or
subtract.

You can use your calculator to work out
the answer, or use written addition and
subtraction.

You can check your answer using opposite
calculations.

Worked example

2 Marcus is paid £2,400 per month after tax.
His bills are:

rent	£720
electricity and gas	£82
council tax	£95
telephone	£32
water	£28

How much does he have left after paying his bills?

720 + 82 + 95 + 32 + 28 = £957
2400 – 957 = £1,443
Marcus has £1,443 left.

To work out how much Marcus spends on
bills, you need to **add** the amounts.

To work out how much he has left, you
need to **subtract**.

You can also check your answer by seeing
if it is sensible.

Now try this

1 Jennifer sells her car for £799 and a car seat
for £34
Out of the money she makes, she buys a new
laptop for £399 and a keyboard for £30
How much money does Jennifer have left?

2 In one day, a shop takes £3,923. Its outgoings
are £2,437. How much profit does the shop
make in the day?

Outgoings are the amount that
is spent on goods or staff.

3 The table shows the number of clients a
plumbing business had each week in February.

Week 1	163
Week 2	78
Week 3	121
Week 4	101

In March, the company had 506 clients.
How many more clients did the company
have in March than February?

Multiplication and division

You need to be able to decide whether a problem asks you to multiply or divide.

Worked example

1 (a) There are 28 cans of drink in a box. A shop buys 24 boxes. How many cans does the shop buy altogether?

$28 \times 24 = 672$ cans

(b) Alana buys 4 packets of football stickers. Each packet contains 6 stickers. Each page of her sticker book has space for 8 stickers. How many pages can Alana fill?

$4 \times 6 = 24$ stickers

$24 \div 8 = 3$

Alana can fill 3 pages.

You can check your answer using opposite calculations.

(a) $28 \times 24 = 672$

so $672 \div 24 = 28$ ✓

(b) $4 \times 6 \div 8 = 3$

so $3 \times 8 \div 6 = 4$ ✓

Worked example

2 The wholesale cost of a bottle of shampoo is £0.94

A shop buys 130 bottles of the shampoo and sells them for £2.40 each. If the shop sells all of the bottles, how much profit will it make?

profit for one bottle:
£2.40 – £0.94 = £1.46

profit for 130 bottles:
£1.46 × 130 = £189.80

Problem solved!

Work out the profit made from one bottle.
To do this, calculate the sale price minus the cost price.
Multiply the profit by the number of bottles sold.
Don't forget to write your answer in pounds.

Now try this

1 312 chairs are to be set up in 6 rows of equal length. How many chairs will be in each row?

2 A minibus can hold 52 people. Joe thinks that he needs 5 minibuses to take 260 people on a trip. Is Joe correct? Explain your reasoning.

3 A shop buys watches for £112 each and sells them for £140. If the shop sells 25 watches, how much profit will it make?

Brackets

If you need to do a calculation with more than one part, it is important that you choose the right order of operations. Brackets around part of the calculation tell you to work out that part first.

The order of operations

 Work out anything within brackets.

 Do any division and multiplication. You can do these two operations in any order – the answer will still be the same.

 Do any addition or subtraction.

Write out each step of the calculation. This makes it easier to check your working.

Worked example

1 Work out these calculations.

(a) $5 \times 0 + 3 = 0 + 3$
$\qquad\qquad\quad = 3$

(b) $(16 - 7) \times 4 = 9 \times 4$
$\qquad\qquad\qquad = 36$

(c) $(15 - 3) \div (3 \times 2) = 12 \div 6$
$\qquad\qquad\qquad\qquad = 2$

Worked example

2 Write $+$, $-$, $\times$ or $\div$ in each box to make these calculations true.

(a) $(8 \boxplus 2) \boxtimes 6 = 60$

(b) $(8 \boxminus 2) \boxdiv 6 = 1$

 Try out some combinations until you get the correct answer. Remember that the operation in the brackets is worked out first.

Worked example

3 A hairdresser charges £30 for a haircut and £70 for highlights. In one week, he does 12 highlights and 25 haircuts.

How much money does the hairdresser take in one week?

 Some calculators let you type in the whole calculation. It is a good idea to check your answer by working it out in steps too.

$(12 \times 70) + (25 \times 30) = 840 + 750$
$\qquad\qquad\qquad\qquad\quad = £1,590$

Now try this

1 Work out the answers to these calculations.
   (a) $4 \times (5 + 2)$ (b) $(6 + 12) \div (12 - 3)$
2 This table shows the ticket prices for a theatre performance. The box office sells 32 adult tickets, 20 child tickets and 15 senior tickets. How much money does the theatre take for this performance?

	Ticket price
adult	£35
child	£12
senior	£14

Multiples, factors and primes

Knowing facts about factors, multiples and prime numbers can help you solve problems.

Factors

The **factors** of a number are the whole numbers that divide into it exactly. 1 and the number itself are both factors of every number.

The factors of 24 are 1, 2, 3, 4, 6, 8, 12 and 24

The factors of a number come in pairs. When you multiply the pairs together, the answer is the number.

The factor pairs of 24 are 1 and 24, 2 and 12, 3 and 8, and 4 and 6

A **common factor** is a number that is a factor of two or more numbers.

3 is a common factor of 9 and 18

Multiples

The **multiples** of a number are all the numbers in its times table.

The multiples of 8 are 8, 16, 24, 32...

A **common multiple** is a number that is a multiple of two or more numbers.

The multiples of 3 are 3, 6, 9, 12, 15...

The multiples of 6 are 6, 12, 18, 24...

6 and 12 are common multiples of 3 and 6 because they are in both lists.

6 is called the **lowest common multiple** as it is the smallest number in both lists.

Worked example

On Mondays, a restaurant gives every 8th table a free dessert and every 12th table a free drink. Which table will be the first to receive both free gifts?

Tables that receive a free dessert:
8, 16, (24), 32, ...

Tables that receive a free drink:
12, (24), 36, ...

The 24th table will be the first to receive both free gifts.

List the multiples of 8 and the multiples of 12. Look for the first number that occurs in both lists.

Primes

A prime number is a number with exactly two factors. It can only be divided by 1 and by itself.

The first 10 prime numbers are:

2, 3, 5, 7, 11, 13, 17, 19, 23, 29

1 is not a prime number as it only has one factor.

Now try this

1 Here is a list of numbers: 5, 7, 16, 18, 28, 41, 72
   From the list, write down:
   (a) a number that is a multiple of 8 and a factor of 32   **(b)** two prime numbers.

2 Music FM broadcasts a travel report every 36 minutes and Sport FM broadcasts one every 24 minutes. They both broadcast a report at 14:30. What time do they next both broadcast a travel report at the same time?

9

Rounding whole numbers

It can be useful to round a number when you don't need to know or use its exact value. Numbers that are rounded are easier to use in estimations.

How to round numbers

When you are rounding numbers, you need to think about place value.

Always look to the place value position to the right of the one you are rounding to.

If this digit is 4 or less, round down. If it is 5 or more, round up.

To round to the nearest 10, look at the units.

To round to the nearest 100, look at the tens.

To round to the nearest 1000, look at the hundreds.

Worked example

1 **(a)** A length of ribbon measures 462 cm. Round this to the nearest 10 cm.

462 cm rounded to the nearest 10 cm is 460 cm.

(b) 17 482 people attended a football game. Round this to the nearest 100

17 482 rounded to the nearest 100 is 17 500

(c) An elephant weighs 4500 kg. Round this to the nearest 1000 kg.

4500 kg rounded to the nearest 1000 kg is 5000 kg.

Worked example

2

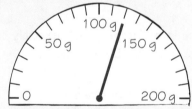

This scale shows the reading for the weight of a hamster. Round this weight to the nearest 100 g.

The scale shows 120 g. 120 g to the nearest 100 g is 100 g.

The reading on the scale is closer to 100 g than to 200 g.

Now try this

1 Liverpool has a population of 473 121
   Round this to the nearest:
   (a) 1000   **(b)** 10 000

2 A new leisure centre cost a total of £1,554,678 to build.
   Round this to the nearest:
   (a) £100,000   **(b)** £1,000,000

3 A swimming pool has a capacity of 375 982 litres.
   Round this to the nearest:
   (a) 100 litres   **(b)** 1000 litres

Fractions

Fractions appear in lots of types of questions.
Here is the flag of Austria.
Two parts are red out of three parts in total, so $\frac{2}{3}$ of the flag is red.

Writing fractions

A pizza is cut into six **equal** pieces.

One piece of pizza = $\frac{1}{6}$

Two pieces = $\frac{2}{6}$ or $\frac{1}{3}$

The whole pizza = $\frac{6}{6}$ or 1

Recognising fractions in words

You should be able to recognise fractions written in words.

a half = $\frac{1}{2}$ two thirds = $\frac{2}{3}$

three quarters = $\frac{3}{4}$ twelve tenths = $\frac{12}{10}$

Worked example

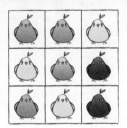

(a) What fraction of these birds are yellow?

$\frac{3}{9} = \frac{1}{3}$

(b) What fraction of these birds are not yellow?

$\frac{6}{9} = \frac{2}{3}$

Three out of nine birds are yellow and six out of nine birds are not yellow.

Notice that the birds that are not yellow + the birds that are yellow = $\frac{3}{9} + \frac{6}{9}$

$= \frac{9}{9}$

$= 1$

Now try this

1 What fraction of the pattern is shaded blue?

2 A chef needs $\frac{1}{4}$ kg of tomatoes for a recipe. The shop sells boxes of tomatoes in these quantities:

$\frac{1}{5}$ kg $\frac{1}{3}$ kg $\frac{1}{6}$ kg $\frac{1}{2}$ kg $\frac{1}{8}$ kg

Which one box should he buy to ensure he has enough tomatoes with the smallest amount left over?

Simplifying fractions

Make sure you can recognise equivalent fractions and write fractions in their simplest form.

Equivalent fractions

Different fractions can describe the same amount. These are called equivalent fractions.

$\frac{1}{2}$ of a pizza is the same amount as $\frac{2}{4}$ of a pizza. You can find equivalent fractions by multiplying or dividing the numerator and denominator by the same number.

Simplifying fractions

If you are asked to write a fraction in its simplest form, find the highest common factor of the numerator and the denominator. Divide both numbers by this factor. The fraction will now be in its simplest form.

$$\frac{18}{27} = \frac{2}{3}$$

$\div 9$

See page 9 for more about common factors.

Worked example

1 Kelly works out how much oil is wasted at two garages one month. The Scunthorpe Street garage wastes $\frac{15}{40}$ of a can. The Grimsby Road garage wastes $\frac{4}{8}$ of a can. Which garage wastes more oil?

$\frac{15}{40} = \frac{3}{8}$ so Grimsby Road wastes more oil.

Find equivalent fractions so that both numbers have the same denominator. Divide 15 and 40 by 5 to get $\frac{3}{8}$ Then, compare the numerators to find which fraction is larger.

Worked example

2 Write $\frac{20}{80}$ as a fraction in its simplest form.

$\frac{20}{80} = \frac{2}{8} = \frac{1}{4}$

When you simplify a fraction in more than one step, write down all of your steps.

Now try this

1 Complete these equivalent fractions.
 (a) $\frac{4}{7} = \frac{?}{14}$ (b) $\frac{1}{2} = \frac{3}{?}$

2 Using any combination of the numbers 1, 4, 8, 10 or 12, write a fraction equivalent to $\frac{2}{3}$

3 Write the fraction $\frac{24}{42}$ in its simplest form.

Mixed numbers

Mixed numbers have a whole number part and a fraction part.

$4\frac{1}{3}$ is the same as 4 and $\frac{1}{3}$

Improper fractions have a numerator larger than their denominator.

$\frac{7}{2}$, $\frac{10}{3}$ and $\frac{21}{5}$ are all improper fractions.

Converting between mixed numbers and improper fractions

To convert a mixed number to an improper fraction...

Multiply the whole number...

...by the denominator...   ...and add it to the numerator.

$3\frac{1}{4} = \frac{(3 \times 4) + 1}{4} = \frac{13}{4}$

Keep the same denominator.

To convert an improper fraction to a mixed number...

Divide the numerator...   Write the remainder as the numerator.

...by the denominator.

$\frac{23}{5} = 23 \div 5 = 4\frac{3}{5}$

Keep the same denominator.

Divide the numerator by the denominator.

Worked example

1 (a) Change $3\frac{2}{3}$ into an improper fraction.

$\frac{3 \times 3 + 2}{6} = \frac{11}{6}$

(b) Change $\frac{28}{5}$ into a mixed number.

$28 \div 5 = 5 \text{ r } 3$ so $\frac{28}{5} = 5\frac{3}{5}$

Worked example

Change $4\frac{5}{6}$ into an improper fraction.

2 Which is larger, $\frac{31}{6}$ or $4\frac{5}{6}$?

$4\frac{5}{6} = \frac{29}{6}$ and $\frac{31}{6} = 5\frac{1}{6}$ so $\frac{31}{6}$ is larger.

Golden rule

Convert mixed numbers to improper fractions before calculating with them.

Now try this

1 (a) Write $5\frac{2}{3}$ as an improper fraction.

(b) Write $\frac{22}{8}$ as a mixed number in its simplest form.

2 Which is smaller, $4\frac{3}{5}$ or $\frac{21}{5}$?

Fractions of amounts

You need to be able to find fractions of amounts to solve different types of problems.

Fractions of amounts

$\frac{1}{3}$ of £180

£60	£60	£60

←——— £180 ———→

£180 ÷ 3 = £60 divide by the denominator

$\frac{3}{4}$ of £360

£90	£90	£90	£90

←——— £360 ———→

£360 ÷ 4 = £90 divide by the denominator

90 × 3 = £270   multiply by the numerator

Worked example

1 (a) $\frac{1}{4}$ of £200

£200 ÷ 4 = £50

(b) $\frac{2}{5}$ of 120 cm

120 cm ÷ 5 = 24 cm

24 cm × 2 = 48 cm

For fractions with a numerator of 1, divide by the denominator.
For other fractions, first divide by the denominator, and then multiply your answer by the numerator.

Worked example

2 Carl has seen a TV that he likes in two shops.

TV Supermarket
$\frac{3}{5}$ of normal price
Normal price £200

TV Sales Store
$\frac{3}{4}$ of normal price
Normal price £180

He wants to pay the least amount of money.
From which shop should he buy the TV? Give your reasons.

TV Supermarket

$\frac{3}{5}$ of £200

£200 ÷ 5 = £40

£40 × 3 = £120

TV Sales Store

$\frac{3}{4}$ of £180

£180 ÷ 4 = £45

£45 × 3 = £135

Carl should buy his TV at TV Supermarket as it has the cheapest price.

Problem solved!

Carl wants to pay the least amount of money so you need to work out how much the TV costs at each store.

✓ Show your working out for each store clearly.

✓ Check your calculations to make sure you haven't made a mistake.

✓ Make a decision based on your calculations. Write a sentence to explain your reasons.

Now try this

1 Which is smaller, $\frac{3}{5}$ of £85 or $\frac{2}{3}$ of £66?

2 Rhoslyn spent £2,100 on a deposit for a flat and some furniture. $\frac{3}{7}$ of the money was spent on the deposit for the flat. The rest was spent on furniture. How much did Rhoslyn spend on furniture?

Decimals

You will need to be able to order decimals in lots of different contexts including money, lengths and weights.

You can use a place value diagram to help you understand and compare decimal numbers. Remember that decimal numbers with more digits are not necessarily bigger. Try writing extra zeros so that all the numbers have the same number of decimal places.

units		tenths	hundredths	thousandths
0	.	3	5	2
0	.	3	6	0
0	.	3	9	0
0	.	4	0	0

The value of 5 in this number is 5 hundredths.

0.36 is the same as 0.360

0.360 is bigger than 0.352 because 6 hundredths is bigger than 5 hundredths.

0.39 is smaller than 0.4 because the digit in the tenths place is smaller.

Worked example

1 Write the value of the digit 4 in:

(a) 5.24   4 hundredths

(b) 36.432   4 tenths

(c) 126.894   4 thousandths

2 Which of these numbers is larger?

(a) 0.0425 or 0.402   0.402

(b) 1.003 or 1.03   1.03

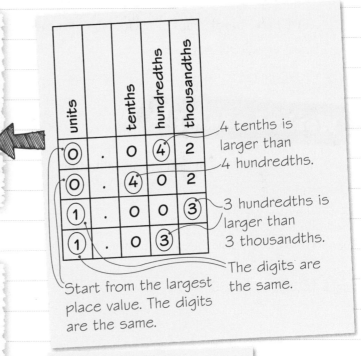

4 tenths is larger than 4 hundredths.

3 hundredths is larger than 3 thousandths.

The digits are the same.

Start from the largest place value. The digits are the same.

Worked example

3 A dressmaker has some lengths of ribbon. Order the lengths from smallest to largest.

0.83 m, 0.083 m, 0.308 m, 0.38 m, 0.038 m

0.038 m, 0.083 m, 0.308 m, 0.38 m, 0.83 m

Compare the digits in each place value position.

Now try this

1 For each pair of numbers, decide which is larger.

(a) 8.7 and 8.274   (b) 42.314 and 42.34   (c) 1.06 and 1.006

2 What is the value of the 6 in these numbers?

(a) 54.056   (b) 0.625

3 The capacities of different water tanks are listed below. Order the capacities from smallest to largest.

9.921 litres   9.219 litres   9.29 litres   9.0912 litres   9.192 litres

Decimal calculations

You need to be able to add, subtract, multiply and divide decimals. You may need to convert money given in pence into pounds and pence before using your calculator.

Worked example

1 Here is a price list for a cafe.

cup of coffee	£1.10
cup of tea	90p
sandwich	£1.99
biscuit	98p

Make sure the amounts are in the same units before performing any calculations.

Convert all of the amounts in pence to pounds.

A cup of tea costs 90p or £0.90

A biscuit costs 98p or £0.98

(a) The cafe sells 20 cups of coffee, 11 cups of tea, 5 sandwiches and 3 biscuits. How much money does the cafe take?

$(20 \times £1.10) + (11 \times £0.90) + (5 \times £1.99) + (3 \times £0.98)$
$= £22 + £9.90 + £9.95 + £2.94$
$= £44.79$

(b) Charlie bought cups of tea for her colleagues. She spent £5.40. How many cups of tea did she buy?

$£5.40 \div £0.90 = 6$

Worked example

2 Below is the price of entry to an exhibition.

adult   £10.95
child   £5.20

(a) Work out the difference in price between the adult and child ticket.

$£10.95 - £5.20 = £5.75$

(b) Work out the cost of an adult ticket and three child tickets.

$£10.95 + £5.20 + £5.20 + £5.20$
$= £26.55$
or
$£10.95 + 3 \times £5.20 = £26.55$

You can either add three lots of the child ticket price or multiply it by 3.

Now try this

1 Mike wants to build a fence around his allotment. He needs to leave space for a gate of 1.5 m. What length of fencing does he need to buy?

2 The receipts show the amounts that Jenny and Nav spent whilst out shopping.
Work out the difference between how much Jenny and Nav spent in pence.

8.48 m

15.4 m

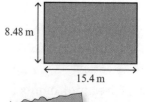

Jenny
£31.99
80p
£23.75

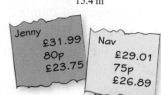

Nav
£29.01
75p
£26.89

Rounding decimals

Your calculator might display an answer with lots of decimal places, particularly when dividing or calculating with fractions and decimals. It is often useful to round this number to the nearest whole number or to 1 or 2 decimal places.

Rounding decimals

Look at the whole numbers that the decimal lies between.

2.6 lies between 2 and 3

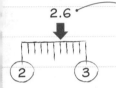

2.6 is closer to 3, so 2.6 rounds up to 3

4.25 lies between 4 and 5

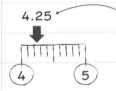

4.25 is closer to 4, so 4.25 rounds down to 4

When the number is exactly halfway between the whole numbers, always round up.

Worked example

1 (a) The length of a bus is 8.6 m. Round this to the nearest metre.

8.6 rounded to the nearest whole number is 9

9 m

(b) A bag of potatoes weighs 3.25 kg. Round this to the nearest kilogram.

3.25 rounded to the nearest whole number is 3

3 kg

(c) In a shop a dress costs £57.50. Round this to the nearest pound.

57.50 rounded to the nearest whole number is 58

£58

Worked example

2 Round 4.374523 to:

(a) 1 decimal place

4.4

(b) 2 decimal places

4.37

To round to 2 decimal places, look at the third digit after the decimal point. 4 is smaller than 5, so round down.

Golden rule

	up	down
Nearest whole number	≥ 0.5	< 0.5
To 1 decimal place (1 dp)	≥ 0.05	< 0.05
To 2 decimal places (2 dp)	≥ 0.005	< 0.005
< less than	≥ greater than or equal to	

Now try this

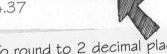

1 Round these numbers to the nearest whole number.
   (a) 9.4   (b) 87.613   (c) 11.94
2 Round these numbers to both 1 and 2 decimal places.
   (a) 4.283458   (b) 0.5073824   (c) 2.098293

Estimation

Estimating the answer to a calculation is useful when you don't need to know the exact answer. You need to be able to round numbers so that you can estimate the answer to a problem.

Rounding

When you estimate, you need to round the numbers first.

Round the numbers to the nearest whole number, 10 or 100 and then do the calculation.

✓ If the number is between 0 and 10, round to the nearest whole number.

✓ If the number is between 10 and 99, round to the nearest 10

✓ If the number is between 100 and 999, round to the nearest 100

> For more about rounding, see pages 10 and 17

The ≈ symbol is used when rounding and estimating. It means 'is approximately equal to'.

Worked example

1 (a) Work out an estimate for 5.8 + 31.4

5.8 ≈ 6 (nearest whole number)
31.4 ≈ 30 (nearest 10)

5.8 + 31.4 ≈ 6 + 30
≈ 36

(b) Work out an estimate for 429 − 28.7

429 ≈ 400 (nearest 100)
28.7 ≈ 30 (nearest 10)

429 − 28.7 ≈ 400 − 30
≈ 370

Use the ≈ sign to show that your answer is not precise.

Worked example

2 A shop sells T-shirts for £36.99 each and scarves for £21.50 each. John buys 12 T-shirts and 12 scarves. Estimate how much this will cost.

cost = 12 × (36.99 + 21.50)
≈ 10 × (40 + 20)
≈ 600

The cost is approximately £600

Problem solved!

Check that you understand what the question is asking you to do.
Show that you have rounded each value.
12 ≈ 10 (nearest 10)
36.99 ≈ 40 (nearest 10)
21.50 ≈ 20 (nearest 10)
Use these values to find an estimate of the cost.

Now try this

1 Estimate the answer to:
  (a) 892 − 31.2   **(b)** 48.3 × 9.6   **(c)** 37 ÷ 2.2

2 Peter sold 89 USB sticks at £24.20 each and 42 USB sticks at £29.50. Each USB stick cost him £11.40. Estimate how much profit he made.

Checking your answer

It is easy to press the wrong button on your calculator and make a mistake. You should always check your answer is correct.

Using estimation

You can use estimation after doing a calculation to check if your answer is sensible.

> **See page 18 for more about estimation.**

> The estimate tells you the answer should be approximately 3400. This is much higher than Maria's answer, so she has probably made a mistake.

Worked example

1 Maria says the answer to
2645 + 841 − 383 is 1345
Use estimation to check whether she is correct.

$2645 \approx 3000$
$841 \approx 800$
$383 \approx 400$
$3000 + 800 - 400 = 3400$

Maria made a mistake in her calculation.

Using inverse operations

You can check your answer is correct by using inverse operations.

✓ Adding and subtracting are inverse operations.

✓ Multiplying and dividing are inverse operations.

Worked example

2 Liam said the answer to 9340 − 835 is 8505
Check whether he is correct using inverse operations.

$9340 - 835 = 8505$ so $8505 + 835 = 9340$

Liam is correct.

> You should always get the number you started with.

Worked example

3 Joshua worked out 49 × 6 and got the answer 284
Check whether he is correct.

If $49 \times 6 = 284$ then $284 \div 6$ must equal 49
$284 \div 6 = 47.3$

Joshua is not correct.

> You could also check by working out
> $284 \div 49$
> You will have a calculator in the test so you can use it to check your answer.

Now try this

1 Joseph worked out this calculation: $823 \times 2.8 - 1289 = 6095$
Show that he is incorrect by estimating the answer to the calculation.

2 Use inverse operations to check that these are correct.
(a) $1423 + 1239 = 2662$ **(b)** $39 + 1323 = 1335$
(c) $53 \times 31 = 1590$ **(d)** $10028 \div 23 = 436$

Fractions and decimals

One way to compare and order fractions is by writing them as decimals.

Writing a fraction as a decimal

Fractions can be read as the numerator divided by the denominator.

$\frac{2}{10}$ means 2 is divided by 10

A fraction looks similar to the divide sign. This will help you remember.

Worked example

1 Write these fractions as decimals.

(a) $\frac{3}{25}$

$3 \div 25 = 0.12$

(b) $\frac{5}{16}$

$5 \div 16 = 0.3125$

> Divide the numerator by the denominator. You can use your calculator to do this.

> Sometimes, your answer will have lots of decimal places. You can round these numbers. The question will tell you how many decimal places to round to.
>
> For example, $8 \div 24 = 0.3333333333...$ which can be rounded to 0.33

2 Order these fractions from smallest to largest.

$\frac{12}{30}$ $\qquad$ $\frac{234}{520}$ $\qquad$ $\frac{8}{24}$

$12 \div 30 = 0.4$ $\qquad$ $234 \div 520 = 0.45$

$8 \div 24 = 0.33$

$\frac{8}{24}$ $\qquad$ $\frac{12}{30}$ $\qquad$ $\frac{234}{520}$

Worked example

3 The weights of some parcels are listed below. Order the weights from smallest to largest.

$1\frac{2}{5}$ kg, $\qquad$ $2\frac{1}{3}$ kg, $\qquad$ $1\frac{3}{10}$ kg, $\qquad$ $2\frac{3}{5}$ kg

$1\frac{2}{5}$ kg = 1.4 kg $\qquad$ $2\frac{1}{3}$ kg = 2.33 kg

$1\frac{3}{10}$ kg = 1.3 kg $\qquad$ $2\frac{3}{5}$ kg = 2.6 kg

$1\frac{3}{10}$ kg, $\qquad$ $1\frac{2}{5}$ kg, $\qquad$ $2\frac{1}{3}$ kg, $\qquad$ $2\frac{3}{5}$ kg

> Write the fractions as decimals and then compare.
>
> $1\frac{2}{5} = 1 + \frac{2}{5}$
>
> $\frac{2}{5}$ can be written as $2 \div 5 = 0.4$
>
> So $1\frac{2}{5} = 1 + 0.4 = 1.4$

Now try this

1 Write these fractions as decimals.

(a) $\frac{4}{5}$ $\qquad$ **(b)** $\frac{27}{20}$ $\qquad$ **(c)** $1\frac{8}{40}$ $\qquad$ **(d)** $2\frac{9}{12}$

2 Order these weights from smallest to largest.

$\frac{5}{8}$ kg $\qquad$ 0.75 kg $\qquad$ 0.4 kg $\qquad$ $\frac{7}{16}$ kg

3 James bought 1.6 kg of potatoes. He used $\frac{3}{4}$ kg in a recipe. What weight of potatoes does he have left?

Percentages

Percentages are useful when comparing proportions of different amounts.
'Per cent' means 'out of 100'. You can write a percentage as a fraction over 100

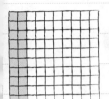   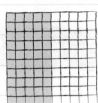   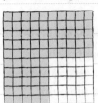   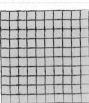

$20\% = \dfrac{20}{100} = \dfrac{1}{5}$ $50\% = \dfrac{50}{100} = \dfrac{1}{2}$ $75\% = \dfrac{75}{100} = \dfrac{3}{4}$ $100\% = \dfrac{100}{100} = 1$

Writing one number as a percentage of another

To write an amount as a percentage of another, first write as a fraction, and then multiply the fraction by 100

Write 63 out of 84 as $\dfrac{63}{84}$

Worked example

1 At a driving school, 84 students are learning to drive. 63 pass the driving test.

What percentage of students pass the test?

$\dfrac{63}{84} \times 100 = (63 \div 84) \times 100$
$= 75\%$

Worked example

2 Carla earns a weekly wage of £400. She spends £100 on rent, £120 on living expenses and saves the rest.

What percentage of her wages does she save?

Carla saves £400 − £100 − £120
= £180
$\dfrac{180}{400} \times 100 = (180 \div 400) \times 100$
$= 45\%$

Problem solved!

✓ Work out how much Carla saves each week.

✓ Write the amount she saves as a fraction of her weekly wage.

✓ Multiply the fraction by 100 to find the percentage.

Now try this

1 Hannah took two physics tests. This table shows her marks for both papers. She needed more than 70% of the total number of marks for both papers to pass. Did Hannah pass the test? Explain your reasoning.

	Hannah's mark	Possible marks
Paper 1	24	30
Paper 2	8	10

2 45 out of 60 workers worked overtime last month. What percentage of workers did **not** work overtime?

3 A manufacturing company stated that less than 5% of its products were faulty. Last month, 911 out of 934 products were functioning correctly and the rest were faulty.
Based on these figures, is the manufacturing company's claim correct?

Percentage calculations

You will be asked to solve problems where you need to work out percentages of an amount and find the result after a **percentage change**.

Percentages with a calculator

To find a percentage of an amount, divide the percentage by 100 to convert it into a decimal and multiply this by the amount.

> You need to find 14% so work out
> 14 ÷ 100 or 0.14
> 14% of £1,500 is 0.14 × £1,500

Worked example

1 One month, Martin spent 14% of his wages on a season ticket. He earns £1,500 per month. How much did he spend on the season ticket?

14 ÷ 100 = 0.14
0.14 × £1,500 = £210

Worked example

2 Pamela buys a car for £3,400 and pays a 15% deposit. How much has she still to pay?

15 ÷ 100 = 0.15
0.15 × 3400 = £510
£3,400 − £510 = £2,890

> Work out 15% of £3,400
> To work out what she still has left to pay, subtract this amount from £3,400

Worked example

3 Nicolette sees a table she likes on sale in two stores.

Table Store: was £90, now 30% off

Furniture Supermarket: was £120, now just 55% of the original price

She wants to pay the cheapest price possible.

Which shop should she buy the table from? Give your reasons.

Table Store	Furniture Supermarket
100 − 30 = 70	55 ÷ 100 = 0.55
70 ÷ 100 = 0.7	0.55 × 120 = £66
0.7 × £90 = £63	

She should buy the table from Table Store as it is £3 cheaper than Furniture Supermarket.

> Make sure you answer the question at the end. Write a sentence to say where she should buy from and why.

Now try this

1 In a competition, the £2,840 prize money is to be shared by the top four contestants. First place gets 45%, second place gets 30% and third place gets 15%. Fourth place gets the remaining prize money. How much does each of the four winners get?

2 There are 1250 members of a gym. 56% are female. How many members are male?

Fractions, decimals and percentages

You can compare fractions, decimals and percentages by changing them to the same type.

Conversion calculations

1 You can convert a decimal to a percentage by multiplying by 100

$$\xrightarrow{\times 100}$$

$0.6 = 60\%$

2 You can write any percentage as a fraction with denominator 100

$60\% = \dfrac{60}{100}$

3 You can convert a fraction to a decimal by dividing the numerator by the denominator.

$\dfrac{3}{5} = 3 \div 5 = 0.6$

Useful equivalents

Remember these common fraction, decimal and percentage equivalents.

Fraction	Decimal	Percentage
$\dfrac{1}{100}$	0.01	1%
$\dfrac{1}{10}$	0.1	10%
$\dfrac{1}{5}$	0.2	20%
$\dfrac{1}{4}$	0.25	25%
$\dfrac{1}{2}$	0.5	50%
$\dfrac{3}{4}$	0.75	75%

Worked example

Felicity has a bag of counters. Of the counters:
5% are red, $\frac{1}{4}$ are blue, $\frac{2}{5}$ are green, and the rest are yellow.
What percentage of the counters are yellow?

$\frac{1}{4} = 25\%$ $\frac{2}{5} = 40\%$

$5 + 25 + 40 = 70$

$100 - 70 = 30$

30% of the counters are yellow.

Problem solved!

The answer needs to be a percentage so convert both fractions into percentages.

The total number of counters is equivalent to 100%, so work out the sum of the other percentages then subtract that from 100% to find the percentage of counters that are yellow.

Now try this

1 A hairdresser conducted a survey to check customer satisfaction. In June, 95% of customers said the service was excellent. In July, 48 out of 52 people said the service was excellent.
Which month had the higher percentage of excellent responses?

2 Write these amounts in order, starting with the smallest: $\frac{3}{5}$ 62%   0.356

3 In a game, 8 players each put 30 counters on a table. Kalinda wins 15% of the counters. Karthik wins $\frac{5}{12}$ of the counters. Cary wins the remaining counters. How many counters did Cary win?

Percentage change

You need to be able to find a new amount after a given percentage change.

Calculating percentage change

There are two methods that you can use to increase or decrease an amount by a certain percentage. If you are asked to work out the cost of an item that was £280 and had 26% off, there are two methods you can use:

Method 1 (subtracting)

Work out 26% of £280:

$\frac{26}{100} \times 280 = £72.80$

Subtract the percentage decrease:

£280 − £72.80 = £207.20

Method 2 (multiplier)

100% − 26% = 74%

$\frac{74}{100} = 0.74$

The multiplier for a 26% decrease is 0.74:

£280 × 0.74 = £207.20

Worked example

1. A football club increases the prices of its season tickets by 5% each year. In 2015, a season ticket cost £650. Calculate the price of this season ticket in 2016

$5\% \text{ of } £650 = \frac{5}{100} \times £650$

$= £32.50$

£650 + £32.50 = £682.50

You could also use this method:

100% + 5% = 105%

$\frac{105}{100} = 1.05$

£650 × 1.05 = £682.50

Worked example

2. Kaz buys a car. The normal price of the car is £7,200 plus VAT at 20%. Kaz gets a 12% discount off the total price including VAT.
   Work out how much Kaz pays for the car.

$20\% \text{ of } £7,200 = \frac{20}{100} \times £7,200 = £1,440$

£7,200 + £1,440 = £8,640

$12\% \text{ of } £8,640 = \frac{12}{100} \times £8,640$

$= £1036.80$

£8,640 − £1,036.80 = £7,603.20

To answer this question, you need to calculate two percentage changes. The discount applies to the total price including VAT, so work out the cost with VAT first. Then subtract 12% of this amount.

Now try this

1. The normal cost of a jumper is £64. In a sale, the cost of the jumper is reduced by 36%. Work out the sale price of the jumper.

2. A train company will increase its fares by 8% next year. The cost of an annual season ticket from London to Watford is currently £7,110 Work out the cost after the increase.

Ratio

Ratios are used to compare quantities.

Writing ratios

Here are six peppers.

The ratio of green to red to yellow is $1:3:2$

The sum of the parts of this ratio is the number of items there are in total.

$1 + 3 + 2 = 6$

Equivalent ratios

You can find equivalent ratios by multiplying or dividing both sides by the same number.

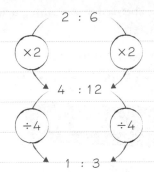

Simplifying ratios

Simplify ratios by dividing both sides of the ratio by the same number.

Divide both sides of the ratio until they no longer have any common factors.

$1:3$, $2:3$ and $3:4$ are all fully simplified.

Golden rule

Always make sure that the values are in the same units and that the numbers are in the correct order in the ratio.

Worked example

Write each ratio in its simplest form.

(a) A garment label says 60% cotton, 20% acrylic, 20% polyester. What is the ratio of cotton to acrylic to polyester?

$60:20:20$

$3:1:1$

(b) A recipe uses 0.25 kg of flour to 150 g of butter. What is the ratio of flour to butter?

$0.25\,\text{kg} = 250\,\text{g}$

$250:150 = 5:3$

Check that the quantities are in the same units but do not include the units in your ratio.

Write the ratios in the order they are given.

Simplify the ratios fully.

Now try this

1 Write the missing numbers in these equivalent ratios.
   (a) $12:18 = 2:\boxed{}$ **(b)** $5:3 = \boxed{}:27$

2 Martin spent 45 minutes swimming and 1.25 hours in the gym. Write the amount of time he spent swimming compared to the time he spent in the gym as a ratio in its simplest form.

3 A bag contains white and pink marshmallows in the ratio $3:4$. What fraction of the sweets are pink?

Ratio problems

Ratio is used in lots of problem-solving questions. You can answer most ratio questions by working out what one part of the ratio represents.

Finding one part of the ratio

There are two ways to find out what one part of the ratio represents.

If you know the total amount, add up all of the parts of the ratio and divide the total amount by this number.

If you know how much one side of the ratio is worth, divide this amount by the number of parts on that side of the ratio.

Worked example

1 Lizzie and Nick are buying a new wardrobe.
   They pay in the ratio 2 : 3
   If Lizzie pays £194, how much does Nick pay?

   194 ÷ 2 = 97

   3 × 97 = 291

   Nick pays £291

Lizzie pays £194 and this is two parts of the whole, so divide £194 by 2 to find out what one part is worth.

Multiply this by 3 to find out how much Nick pays.

Worked example

2 Alexis, Nisha and Paul share a flat. One month, their electricity bill is £120
   They decide to split the bill in the ratio 3 : 5 : 2
   How much does Alexis pay?

   3 : 5 : 2 = 10

   120 ÷ 10 = 12

   3 × 12 = 36   so Alexis pays £36

Add up the parts of the ratio to find out the total number of parts. Divide the total amount by this to find what one part of the ratio is worth.

Now try this

1 The ratio of adults to children who visited a museum in March was 2 : 3
   (a) If 56 adults visited the museum in March, how many children visited?
   (b) What was the total number of visitors in March?
2 A company donate a proportion of their profits to an education charity and a homeless shelter in the ratio 7 : 3. Last year they gave away £8,000 altogether. How much more did they give to the education charity than the homeless shelter?
3 A bag contains red, green and yellow sweets in the ratio 4 : 3 : 2
   There are 72 red sweets in the bag.
   What is the total number of sweets in the bag?

Proportion

Direct proportion

Two quantities are in **direct proportion** when both quantities increase at the same rate.

number of theatre tickets bought — total cost

3 — £135
×3 — ×3
9 — £405

Worked example

1 Jo buys five tickets for a total of £206.25
How much would it cost her to buy seven?

cost of one ticket: £206.25 ÷ 5 = £41.25
cost of seven tickets: £41.25 × 7 = £288.75

The number of tickets and the total cost are in direct proportion.

First find out how much each ticket costs, and then multiply by 7 to find the total.

Worked example

Calculate the cost of one picture frame first. Then multiply the cost of one frame by 7 to work out the cost of seven frames.

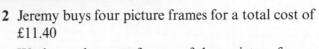

2 Jeremy buys four picture frames for a total cost of £11.40
Work out the cost of seven of these picture frames.

cost of 1 frame = £11.40 ÷ 4 = £2.85
cost of 7 frames = £2.85 × 7 = £19.95

Golden rule

When you are working with money you should:

 do all your calculations in either pounds or pence

 write £ or p in your answer, but not both

 write answers in pounds to 2 decimal places.

Start by working out how much one pair of tap shoes costs. Use this to work out the answers.

Now try this

1 Eight pairs of tap shoes cost £279.60 in total.
(a) Work out the cost of five pairs of tap shoes.
(b) Work out the cost of 12 pairs of tap shoes.
2 Eight identical bottles of water cost £4.48 in total.
Work out the cost of 12 of these bottles of water.

Scaling with ratio

You will use ratio and proportion to scale amounts up or down. Work out the amount for one item first and then scale up or down.

Worked example

1 To make pancakes for six people, you need 100 g flour, 2 eggs and 300 ml milk.

   (a) How much flour is needed to make pancakes for 10 people? Give your answer to the nearest gram.

   1 person: 100 ÷ 6 = 16.67 g
   10 people: 16.67 g × 10 = 167 g
   (to nearest gram)

   (b) Ellie has 7 eggs and plenty of the other ingredients.

   How many people can she make pancakes for?

   7 ÷ 2 = 3.5
   Ellie can make 3.5 lots of the recipe.
   3.5 × 6 = 21
   She can make pancakes for 21 people.

Find out how much flour is needed for one person.

Multiply this by 10 to find the amount of flour needed for 10 people.

Work out the number that you need to multiply 2 by to get 7. You can do this by calculating 70 ÷ 2

Worked example

2 A garden centre sells plants in trays of 6 or boxes of 10

   Trays of 6 cost £15 and boxes of 10 cost £24

   Work out whether the box or the tray offers better value. Show all your working.

   tray   box
   15 ÷ 6 = 2.5   24 ÷ 10 = 2.4
   £2.50 per plant   £2.40 per plant

   £2.40 is less than £2.50 so the box is better value.

Problem solved!

You need to show **all** your working in this question.

✓ Work out the cost of each plant in a tray of 6

✓ Work out the cost of each plant in a tray of 10

✓ Write a short conclusion saying which one is better value.

Now try this

1 A recipe for vegetable soup uses 480 g of potatoes for six people.
   How many grams of potatoes are needed for eight people?

2 A bag of crisps contains 35 g of fat per 100 g.
   How much fat is in a 230 g bag of crisps?

3 A shop sells packets of raisins. It has two offers.
   Which offer is the best value for money?

offer A	offer B
12 packets for £4.32	18 packets for £6.30

Formulas

A formula is a mathematical rule that lets you calculate one quantity when you know the others.

Reading formulas

You might see formulas written in words or using algebra.

The formula for the area of this triangle is:

Area = $\frac{1}{2}$ × base × height

You may also see this formula written using algebra:

$A = \frac{1}{2} bh$

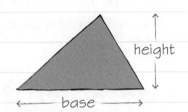

To solve the equation, first substitute in the values you know and then use the correct order of operations to work out the missing value.

Worked example

1 This formula works out the cooking time for beef.

> cooking time in minutes = weight in kg × 42 + 20

Work out the cooking time for a 2 kg joint of beef.

cooking time = 2 × 42 + 20

            = 84 + 20

            = 104

The cooking time is 104 minutes.

Substitute the weight into the formula before you do any calculations.

Remember to use the correct order of operations. Multiply first, then add.

You can give your answer in minutes or in hours and minutes.

Worked example

2 The formula to convert Fahrenheit to Celsius is:

$C = \frac{5}{9}(F - 32)$

where C = Celsius and F = Fahrenheit.
How many degrees Celsius is 77 °F?

$C = \frac{5}{9} \times (77 - 32)$

   $= \frac{5}{9} \times 45$

   $= 25\,°C$

Problem solved!

✓ Substitute the numbers into the formula.
✓ Do the calculation in brackets first.
✓ Do the multiplication and division next.
✓ Check your answer makes sense.

Now try this

This rule is used to work out the cost of hiring a digger: $C = 64D + 109$
(where C is the cost in £ and D is the number of days the digger is hired for).
(a) Alan hires the digger for four days. Work out how much this will cost him.
(b) Alicia wants to hire a digger for six days. She has £500. Can she afford it?

Writing formulas

You need to be able to write word formulas to express mathematical rules.

Word formulas

Jeanette has an annual salary of £16,500 plus £10 commission for each client.

You could write a word formula to describe this:

total salary (£) = 16,500 + 10 × number of clients

Worked example

1 This diagram shows a regular octagon. Write a formula to show the perimeter in terms of the length of one side.

The perimeter is the distance all the way around a shape. All the sides of a regular shape are the same length and an octagon has eight sides.

perimeter = 8 × length of one side

Worked example

2 A plumber charges £28 for every hour she works plus a £35 call-out charge.

   (a) Write a word formula to show the total cost of hiring the plumber.

total cost (£) = 28 × number of hours + 35

The question asks you to write a formula for the total cost of hiring the plumber, so write this on its own on one side of the formula.

   (b) If a job takes four hours, how much will she charge?

total cost = 28 × 4 + 35
           = £147

Use your word formula to answer the question. Substitute in the values you know and use them to work out the total cost.

Now try this

1 This shape is made from three identical square tiles. Write a word formula for the perimeter of the shape.

2 A waiter earns £10 an hour plus tips. Write a word formula for his total wage.

3 Bruce uses this formula to work out how many spoonfuls of coffee grains to put into his coffee machine:
   $n = 2C + 1$
   where n is the number of spoonfuls of coffee grains and C is the number of cups of coffee he wants to make. Bruce wants to make three cups of coffee. How many spoonfuls of coffee grains should he use?

Formula problems

Sometimes you will need to solve problems using formulas.
You can substitute the values you have into the formula to help you find the answer to a problem.

Worked example

1 The formula for working out the monthly wages, w, of a salesperson is $w = b + c$

where b = basic pay and c = commission for sales.

In May, the salesperson earned wages of £3,200. Her basic pay is £2,100.

Work out her commission.

£3,200 = £2,100 + b

£3,200 − £2,100 = b

£1,100 = b

Write down what you know.

w = £3,200

b = £2,100

Substitute the values into the formula.

$w = b + c$

3200 = b + 2100

You know the value of £2,100 + b, so use inverse operations to find the value of b.

See page 19 for more about using inverse operations.

Worked example

2 The formula for working out speed, S, is $S = \frac{D}{T}$.

A car travels at an average speed of 60 km/h for 3 hours. How far has it travelled?

$60 = \dfrac{D}{T}$

$60 \times 3 = D$

$D = 180\,\text{km}$

Substitute the values you know into the formula and then use inverse operations to find the right value.

$\frac{D}{T}$ means $D \div T$, so you can use multiplication to find the value of D.

Now try this

1 A telephone salesperson earns commission of £15 for each successful sale.
   The formula used to work out the total commission received each day, c, is $c = 15s$
   where s = number of successful sales.
   (a) Rohan makes 12 successful sales in one day. Work out his commission.
   (b) Rohan has a target to earn £315 in commission in one day. How many sales must he make?
2 The formula used to work out the profit, p, that a company makes is $p = t - e$
   where t = takings and e = expenses.
   (a) Work out the profit that the company makes in one month if its takings are £12,000 and its expenses are £2,500.
   (b) In one year, the company made a profit of £48,000. Its expenses were £30,000.
       Work out the company's takings in that year.

Problem-solving practice

When you are solving problems, you need to:

✓ read the question

✓ decide which calculation you are going to use

✓ check your answers

✓ make sure you have answered the question asked.

 A music website sells songs and albums.

Songs cost 79p each.

Albums cost £6.99 each.

Aaron has a £25 gift card.

He buys two albums and spends the rest on songs.

How many songs can he afford?

Decimal calculations page 16

Choose whether to work in pounds or pence.

If you get a decimal answer, you will need to round down as Aaron can only buy a whole number of songs.

TOP TIP

Whichever strategy you choose, you have to show your working.

 Claire owns a TV store. She buys 80 TVs to sell in her shop. Claire pays £200 for each TV.

She sells $\frac{2}{5}$ of the TVs for £300 each.

She sells 25% of the TVs for £250 each.

She sells the remaining TVs for £200.

What is the total amount of profit that Claire makes?

Percentage calculations page 22

You need to work out how many TVs she sells for each amount.

TOP TIP

Write short headings to organise your working.

---

3 In 2013, a business used 1800 ink cartridges. In 2014, the same business increased its ink cartridge usage by 20%. In 2015, it decreased its usage by 15% from 2014

(a) Work out how many ink cartridges the business used in 2015

(b) Work out the percentage increase in the ink cartridges used in 2015 from 2013

Percentage change page 24
Percentage calculations page 22

(a) Increase 1800 by 20% and then decrease your answer by 15%.

TOP TIP

Check your answer is sensible.

Problem-solving practice

 A holiday company asked its customers to rate a hotel.

45% of customers said that the hotel was excellent value.

3 out of every 8 customers said the hotel was satisfactory.

The rest were unhappy with the hotel.

What percentage of customers were unhappy with the hotel?

Fractions, decimals and percentages page 23

Write 3 out of 8 as a percentage.

TOP TIP

Check your working as all the percentages should add up to 100%.

 Elinor wants to make some scones.
She has this list of ingredients.

> ### Scones
> 240 g self-raising flour
> 1 tsp baking powder
> 80 g butter
> 160 ml milk

Elinor wants to make as many scones as she can.

She has 120 g of butter.

She has plenty of the other ingredients.

How much self-raising flour should she use?

Scaling with ratio page 28

Work out the scale factor (the number you multiply 80 by to get 120).

This will tell you how many of the scones she can make with 120 g of butter.

TOP TIP

Use the online calculator to do your calculations.

Show your working clearly so that you can answer the question with reasons.

 Kiera the electrician charges £25 per hour of work and a £50 call-out charge.

(a) Write a word formula for the total amount Kiera charges for doing a job.

(b) Jemma books Kiera for a job which takes three hours. How much does it cost her?

(c) On another job, Kiera earns £175. How many hours did she work?

Formulas page 29
Writing formulas page 30

(a) Write the formula starting with

   charge = ...

(b) Substitute the number of hours Kiera worked into the formula you worked out in part (a).

(c) There are different ways you can answer this question. You could use part (b) to help you work out the answer. If Kiera worked three hours for Jemma, how many extra hours did she work to earn £175?

TOP TIP

In the online test, if you get stuck, you can flag a question to come back to later.

Click the review button so that you can check that question again.

 Flag

 Review

Units of time

You need to be able to use time measured in different units and work out how long different tasks take.

Units of time

60 seconds = 1 minute	7 days = 1 week	10 years = 1 decade
60 minutes = 1 hour	52 weeks = 1 year	100 years = 1 century
24 hours = 1 day	365 days = 1 year	

Worked example

1 Noah ordered a cake on Monday 27 April. He was told that it would be ready for collection on Wednesday the following week.

(a) What was the date on Wednesday of the next week?

6 May

(b) Eliza's cake took the same amount of time to prepare. She received it on 4 June. When did she order it?

Noah's cake took 9 days
so Eliza received her cake on 26 May.

> List the days between Monday 27 April and Wednesday the following week.

> Work out how long Noah's cake took to prepare, then count back from 4 June to work out when Eliza ordered hers.

Worked example

2 The table shows the amount of time Warren spent on certain tasks at work.

Task	Time
shelving	2 hours
stock-taking	90 minutes
updating the website	45 minutes

Warren thinks he worked for $4\frac{1}{4}$ hours in total. Is he correct?

stock-taking: 90 minutes = $1\frac{1}{2}$ hours

updating the website: 45 minutes = $\frac{3}{4}$ of an hour

$2 + 1\frac{1}{2} + \frac{3}{4} = 4\frac{1}{4}$ hours so Warren is correct.

> **Golden rule**
>
> To convert from hours to minutes multiply by 60
>
> To convert from minutes to hours divide by 60

> The question asks about the number of hours Warren has worked, so convert from minutes to hours.

Now try this

1 Mary needs to get her wedding dress made. She needs to collect her dress on or before Friday 17 July. The dressmaker needs at least 20 working days to make the dress. She works Monday to Wednesday inclusive. What is the latest day that the dressmaker can start to make the dress?

2 James spends 4.5 hours working and 15 minutes travelling to work. What is the total time James spends travelling and working?

12-hour and 24-hour clock

You need to be able to read both digital and analogue clocks. Digital clocks can display time in two ways, using either the 12- or the 24-hour clock.

12-hour clock	24-hour clock
8:15 a.m.	08:15
4:50 p.m.	16:50
12:00 midday	12:00
12:00 midnight	00:00

In the 12-hour clock, you have to write whether it is morning (a.m.) or afternoon (p.m.).

In the 24-hour clock, you can tell whether the time is afternoon or morning by looking at the first two digits. If the first two digits are 12 or more, the time is in the afternoon. If the first two digits are less than 12, the time is in the morning.

The time is 17 minutes past one in the afternoon.
In the 12-hour clock, this would be written as 1.17 p.m.
In the 24-hour clock, this would be written as 13:17

Worked example

1 Sarah left home at 20 to 8 in the morning to go to work.

(a) Write this time in the 12-hour clock.

7.40 a.m.

(b) She left work at 5:15 p.m. Write this time in the 24-hour clock.

17:15

If the time is in the afternoon, you can convert to the 24-hour clock by adding 12

Worked example

2 A chef put a piece of meat in the oven at 11.45 a.m. It needed to be cooked for 2.5 hours.

Write the time that the meat should be taken out of the oven in:

(a) the 24-hour clock

2.5 hours = 2 hours and 30 minutes

14:15

(b) the 12-hour clock.

2:15 p.m

Don't forget to write a.m. or p.m. for a time in the 12-hour clock.

Now try this

1 Complete this table of times in the 12-hour and 24-hour clock.

12-hour	3:12 a.m.	......	11:30 p.m.	......
24-hour	......	19:50	......	22:15

2 David leaves his office to deliver a parcel at 1:15 p.m. It takes him 80 minutes. What time does he get back to the office? Write the time in the 24-hour clock.

Timetables

You need to be able to read timetables and use them to work out how long journeys will take.

Reading timetables

This table shows part of a bus timetable.

George St	08:15	09:15	10:45	11:15
Blossom St	08:28	09:28	10:58	11:28
Portugal St	08:45	09:45	11:15	11:45
Butler Ave.	09:00	10:00	11:30	12:00

This bus leaves George Street at 10:45 and arrives at Butler Avenue at 11:30

This bus leaves Blossom Street at 11:28 and arrives at Portugal Street at 11:45

Timetables usually give times using the 24-hour clock.

1408 means 14:08

Worked example

This is part of a train timetable from Kenworthy to Lawton.

Kenworthy	1408		1428		1438
Apley	1411		1431		1441
Linley	1414		1434		1444
Haultwick	1417		1437		1447
Lawton	1420		1440		1450

(a) Amos needs to get to Lawton before 14:45. Which is the latest train he could catch from Apley?

14:31

(b) How long does it take to get from Kenworthy to Haultwick?

All the trains take the same amount of time, so find the difference between the arrival time and the departure time for one of the trains.

Depart at 14:08 and arrive at 14:17
Journey time = 9 minutes

(c) Bhavnisha's house is a 10-minute walk from Linley station. She arrives at Kenworthy station 5 minutes early for her train. How long will it be before she gets home?

5 minutes + 6 minutes + 10 minutes = 21 minutes

Now try this

The timetable shows the tram times from Port Street to Newton Road.

Port Street	11:17	11:29	11:41	11:53
Lapwing Lane	11:25	11:37	11:49	12:01
Sefton Village	11:38	11:50	12:02	12:14
Newton Road	11:42	11:54	12:06	12:18

(a) Joan takes the 11:49 tram from Lapwing Lane to Newton Road. She then walks for 18 minutes to get to a restaurant. At what time does she arrive at the restaurant?

(b) David needs to get to a job interview at 12:15. He lives a 5-minute walk from Port Street station and the interview is a 10-minute walk from Sefton Village station. What is the latest time he could leave to make sure he gets to the interview on time?

Creating a time plan

It is important to plan your time so that you manage to do everything that needs to be done.

1 Read the whole question carefully. Try to remember all the rules as you make your time plan.

2 Start by writing in all the activities that need to be done at a certain time. Then write in all the other activities. Make sure there is enough time for each one and they don't overlap.

3 Read the question again line by line and check your time plan follows all the rules.

Worked example

Fergal is planning some activities for a training day for his employees.

There are four activities: a talk, a workshop, a role play and a test.

There are four sessions in the day and three teams.

- Every team must do each activity once.
- Only one team can do an activity in a session.
- All of the teams need to attend the workshop between sessions 1 and 3

Plan the day for Fergal.

	Session 1	Session 2	Session 3	Session 4
Team A	workshop	test	role play	talk
Team B	talk	workshop	test	role play
Team C	role play	talk	workshop	test

Problem solved!

Think about your strategy.

Organise the workshop for all teams first as this can only be scheduled in certain sessions. Then write in the other activities.

When you have finished, check your work.

✓ Check that you have included all the activities for each team for each team.

✓ Make sure that the activities don't overlap.

✓ Check that each group does the workshop between sessions 1 and 3

Now try this

James is organising a day out for his friends. He wants to plan two activities for the morning and two for the afternoon. He has a budget of between £180 and £200 for the day and he wants the activities to last between 5 and 7 hours in total. Plan the activities for James.

Activity	wildlife show	adventure rides	treasure hunt	nature tour	bird sanctuary	arts and crafts
Time	afternoon	morning	afternoon	morning	afternoon	morning
Length	2 hours	1.5 hours	45 mins	1 hour	1.5 hours	1 hour
Cost	£48	£65	£46	£28	£52	£30

Remember to check your answer matches the requirements stated in the question.

37

Had a go ☐   Nearly there ☐   Nailed it! ☐

Problem-solving practice

When you are solving problems, you need to:

✓ read the question
✓ check your answers
✓ decide which calculation you are going to use
✓ make sure you have answered the question asked.

 This table shows the amount of time certain tasks take for a hotel housekeeper to complete.

Task	Time
vacuuming the floors	10 minutes
turning down the bed	15 minutes
cleaning the bathroom	25 minutes
ironing service	45 minutes

In one day, the housekeeper vacuums, turns down the bed and cleans the bathroom in six rooms. He also provides the ironing service for three rooms.

He starts at 06:30 and has a break in the morning for 15 minutes and a lunch break for 45 minutes. At what time does he finish work?

Units of time page 34

Work out the total amount of time spent in minutes and then convert to hours to add on to the start time.

TOP TIP

If the number of hours includes a decimal, remember that the numbers after the decimal point are a **fraction** of the hour, not the number of minutes.

 Here is part of a bus timetable.

Waddington	0815	0845	0915
West Bradford	0830	0900	0930
Grindleton	0850	0920	0950
Sawley	0915	0945	1015

Johanna travels to work from West Bradford to Sawley every day. It takes her 12 minutes to walk from home to the West Bradford bus stop and 11 minutes to walk from the Sawley bus stop to her office.

She needs to get to work before 10:00

What is the latest time she can leave home and get to work on time?

Timetables page 36

Work out which bus Johanna needs to catch to get to work by 10:00

Remember to allow time for her to walk to and from the bus stops.

TOP TIP

In the online test, if you get stuck, you can flag a question to come back to later.

Click the review button so that you can check that question again.

Problem-solving practice

Giles is organising a programme of events for a literature festival. It starts at 11:00 and must finish at 15:00

Here are the events he is choosing from:

• talk by author (1.5 hours)
• live reading of a book (1 hour)
• theatre performance (1 hour 45 mins)
• group discussion (45 mins)
• creative writing workshop (1.25 hours)
• crafts (0.5 hours).

Create a time plan for Giles showing which activities will run at which times. You don't need to include all of the activities but make sure there is always an activity running.

Creating a time plan page 37

Draw a table to write in the times and activities.

Time	Event
11:00	activity 1
	activity 2
15:00	end of day

TOP TIP

Work out how many hours the festival lasts and then add up different combinations of events to find one that will fill the day.

Mark has a business function in London at 18:30

He will travel by train from Manchester to London. The journey takes 4 hours and 40 minutes.

He needs to buy a shirt before getting the train to London. He thinks that he will need $\frac{1}{2}$ hour to shop. He estimates that his journey to the shops will take 20 minutes, and the journey from the shops to the train station will take $\frac{3}{4}$ hour. What time should Mark leave to go to the shops?

Units of time page 34

Find out how much time Mark needs to do his shopping and travel to London.

TOP TIP

Draw a timeline, starting from when Mark needs to arrive at the function in London and working backwards.

The clocks show the time in London and Melbourne. It is morning in London.

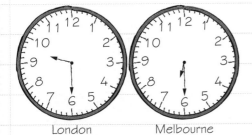

London   Melbourne

(a) Write down the time in London using the 24-hour clock.

(b) When it is morning in London, it is afternoon in Melbourne. How many hours is Melbourne ahead of London?

12-hour and 24-hour clock page 35

Write the times for both London and Melbourne in the 24-hour clock. This will help you work out the time difference.

TOP TIP

Check if your answer is sensible.

Units

Most of the units of measurement used in the UK are metric units, but we sometimes use imperial units too. You need to be able to recognise metric and imperial units and convert between them.

Worked example

1 Write the metric and imperial units that you would use to measure each of the following.

   (a) The distance between two towns

   miles – imperial

   kilometres – metric

   (b) The height of a garden shed

   feet – imperial

   metres – metric

   (c) The weight of a bag of carrots

   pounds – imperial

   grams – metric

   (d) The capacity of a car fuel tank

   gallons – imperial

   litres – metric

Metric and imperial conversions

Length

Imperial units		Metric units
1 mile	≈	1.6 kilometres (km)
1 foot (ft)	≈	30 centimetres (cm)
1 inch (in)	≈	25 millimetres (mm)

Weight

Imperial units		Metric units
1 stone (st)	≈	6 kilograms (kg)
1 pound (lb)	≈	450 grams (g)
1 ounce (oz)	≈	30 grams (g)

Capacity

Imperial units		Metric units
1 gallon (gal)	≈	4.5 litres (l)
1 pint (pt)	≈	0.5 litre (l)

Worked example

2 Estimate each of these in metric and imperial units.

   (a) The height of an average male in the UK

   imperial – 5 ft 10 in

   metric – 1.8 m

   (b) The weight of a bag of sugar

   imperial – 2 lb

   metric – 1 kg

 Estimate first in the units you prefer to use, and then try converting to the other type of units.

Now try this

1 Which imperial and metric units would you use to measure the weight of a car?

2 Which imperial and metric units would you use to measure the capacity of a household boiler?

3 Mike estimates that the height of a double-decker bus is about 7 feet. Do you think that this is a reasonable estimate? Explain why.

4 Estimate the width of an adult thumb. Give your answer in both metric and imperial units.

Scales

You need to be able to read scales and number lines.

Reading a scale

Not all divisions represent 1 unit or 10 units.

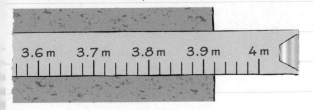

There are 5 divisions between 3.9 m and 4 m.

$0.1 \div 5 = 0.02$

Each division represents 0.02 m.

This table is 3.92 m long.

Estimating the reading on a scale

Sometimes you have to **estimate** the reading on a scale.

The water doesn't come up to an exact mark but you can make an estimate.

The water is closer to 50 ml than it is to 40 ml.

48 ml would be a good estimate.

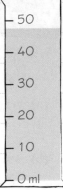

Worked example

The diagram below shows four identical cubes and four identical tetrahedrons.

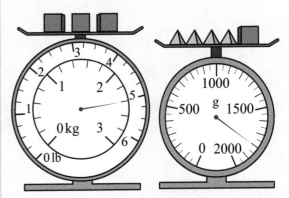

Work out the weight in kg of one tetrahedron.

$2.4 \div 3 = 0.8$ so 1 cube is 0.8 kg

$1800 \text{ g} \div 1000 = 1.8 \text{ kg}$

$1.8 \text{ kg} - 0.8 \text{ kg} = 1 \text{ kg}$

$1 \div 4 = 0.25$ so 1 tetrahedron = 0.25 kg

Problem solved!

Make sure you understand the scales. You need to use metric units, so ignore the measurements in lb on the first scale. Plan your strategy before you start.

- ✓ To work out the weight of one cube, divide the total on the first scale by 3
- ✓ Subtract that from the reading on the second scale.
- ✓ Divide the remainder by 4 to work out the weight of one tetrahedron.

Make sure you write down your working so you can show the strategy you used.

Now try this

This scale has three identical spheres on it.
Work out the weight in grams of one sphere.

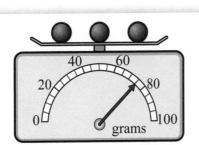

Routes

You can work out the shortest route between places using maps that are not to scale but have the distances labelled. Make sure you understand how to find the best route.

Worked example

The diagram shows the distances between Ann's house and some places she visits regularly.

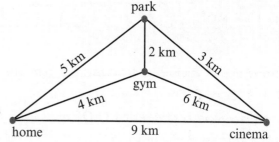

(a) What is the distance between her home and the gym?

4 km

(b) Ann travels 3 km from the park. Which of the locations does she visit?   cinema

(c) Ann goes from her home to the park and then to the gym and then back home. What distance has she travelled?

5 + 2 + 4 = 11 km

(d) Ann wants to visit the park, the gym and the cinema in one day. She starts from home and returns to home. Plan the shortest route.

home to gym, gym to park, park to cinema, cinema to home
    4   + 2   + 3   + 9   = 18 km

Use a system when finding the shortest route.

You want to use the shortest distances so try to avoid passing the same place twice.

Check your answer by adding the distances to make sure it is the shortest route.

Now try this

The diagram shows the distances between four cities in Spain.
  (a) How many miles are between Barcelona and Zaragoza?
  (b) Courtney flies to Barcelona. She wants to visit all the cities by travelling the shortest distance. Plan her journey.

1 mile ≈ 1.6 km

Length

You need to be able to recognise units of length and convert between different units. Metric units of length include kilometres, metres, centimetres and millimetres. Imperial units of length include miles, feet and inches.

Converting between metric units of length

You can convert between metric units of length by multiplying or dividing by 10, 100 or 1000

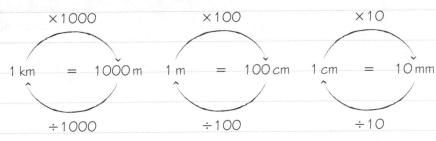

$$\times 1000 \quad\quad\quad \times 100 \quad\quad\quad \times 10$$
$$1\,km = 1000\,m \quad 1\,m = 100\,cm \quad 1\,cm = 10\,mm$$
$$\div 1000 \quad\quad\quad \div 100 \quad\quad\quad \div 10$$

Converting between imperial and metric units

You can convert between metric and imperial units by using the correct conversion factors. You need to be able to use these conversion factors but you don't need to memorise them.

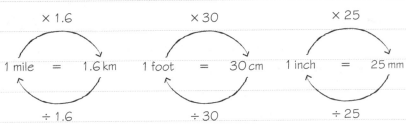

$$\times 1.6 \quad\quad\quad \times 30 \quad\quad\quad \times 25$$
$$1\,mile = 1.6\,km \quad 1\,foot = 30\,cm \quad 1\,inch = 25\,mm$$
$$\div 1.6 \quad\quad\quad \div 30 \quad\quad\quad \div 25$$

Worked example

(a) Convert 4.2 km to metres (m).

→ ×

km	m
1	1000
4.2	4200

4.2 × 1000 = 4200 m

> Draw a table and write down what one unit represents. This number tells you what you need to multiply or divide by.

(b) Convert 32 km to miles.

← ÷

miles	km
1	1.6
20	32

32 ÷ 1.6 = 20 miles

> To change from km to m, × 1000
> To change from m to km, ÷ 1000

Now try this

The mileage chart shows the distance between different cities given in miles.
How many kilometres is Bristol from London?

Brighton			
134	Bristol		
183	124	Derby	
52	117	125	London

Speed

You need to know the relationship between speed, distance and time.

Formula triangle for speed

This is the formula triangle for speed.

$$\text{average speed} = \frac{\text{distance travelled}}{\text{total time taken}}$$

$$\text{time} = \frac{\text{distance}}{\text{speed}}$$

$$\text{distance} = \text{speed} \times \text{time}$$

Using a formula triangle

Cover up the quantity you want to find with your finger. The position of the other two quantities tells you the formula.

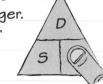

$$T = \frac{D}{S} \qquad S = \frac{D}{T} \qquad D = S \times T$$

Units of speed

The most common units of speed are:

• metres per second (m/s)

• kilometres per hour (km/h)

• miles per hour (mph).

When distance is measured in km and time is measured in hours, speed will be measured in km/h.

Minutes and hours

For questions on speed, you need to be able to convert between minutes and hours.

Remember that there are 60 minutes in every hour.

Half an hour is 30 minutes.

195 minutes is $3\frac{1}{4}$ hours.

Worked example

A plane left Luton airport at 08:00 and arrived at Glasgow airport at 09:15. It travelled at a constant speed of 416 km/h. How far did it travel?

08:00 to 09:15 is 1.25 hours

$D = S \times T$

$= 416 \times 1.25$

$= 520\,km$

Make sure that the units match.

The speed is given in km/h, so convert the time into hours. The units of distance will be km.

Golden rule

☑ Draw a formula triangle.

☑ Make sure the units match.

☑ Give units with your answer.

Now try this

Bradley went on a bike tour. He travelled from Dijon to Macon which is a distance of 130 km. His average speed was 40 km/h.

How long did it take him? Give your answer in hours and minutes.

Weight

You need to be able to recognise units of weight and convert between different units. Metric units of weight include tonnes, kilograms, grams and milligrams.

Converting between metric units of weight

You can convert between metric units of weight by multiplying or dividing by 1000

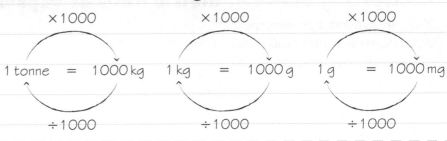

×1000   ×1000   ×1000

1 tonne = 1000 kg   1 kg = 1000 g   1 g = 1000 mg

÷1000   ÷1000   ÷1000

Converting between metric and imperial units of weight

You can also convert between metric and imperial units of weight by using the correct conversion factors. You need to know how to use these conversion factors but you don't need to memorise them.

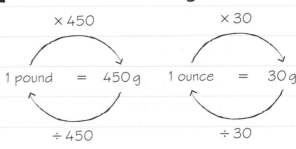

×6   ×450   ×30

1 stone = 6 kg   1 pound = 450 g   1 ounce = 30 g

÷6   ÷450   ÷30

Worked example

(a) Convert 16 kg to milligrams (mg).

⟶ ×

kg	mg
1	1 000 000
16	16 000 000

16 × 1 000 000 = 16 000 000 mg

To change from kg to g, multiply by 1000
To change from g to mg, multiply by 1000
So to change from kg to mg, multiply by
1000 × 1000 = 1 000 000

(b) Convert 1575 g to pounds.

⟵ ÷

pounds	g
1	450
3.5	1575

1575 ÷ 450 ≈ 3.5 pounds

Use the ≈ sign rather than the = sign.
This is because the conversions are
approximate.

Now try this

1 **(a)** Convert 3 kg to stones.   **(b)** Convert 6000 g to ounces.
2 Find the total of these weights: 1800 g, 5.4 kg, 11 pounds
  Give your answer in pounds.

Capacity

Capacity tells you how much something will hold. You need to be able to recognise units of capacity and convert between different units. Metric units of capacity include litres, centilitres and millilitres. Common imperial units for capacity are gallons and pints.

Converting between metric units of capacity

You can convert between metric units of capacity by multiplying or dividing by 10, 100 or 1000

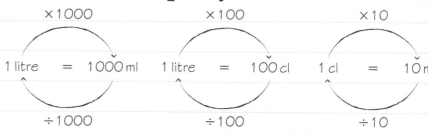

×1000
1 litre = 1000 ml
÷1000

×100
1 litre = 100 cl
÷100

×10
1 cl = 10 ml
÷10

Draw a table and write down what one unit represents. This tells you what you need to multiply or divide by.

To change from ml to cl, divide by 10

Worked example

1 Convert 40 ml to cl.

← ÷

cl	ml
1	10
4	40

40 ÷ 10 = 4 cl

Metric and imperial capacities

You can convert between metric and imperial units of capacity by using the correct conversion factors. You need to know how to use these conversion factors but you don't have to memorise them.

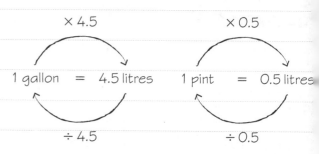

× 4.5
1 gallon = 4.5 litres
÷ 4.5

× 0.5
1 pint = 0.5 litres
÷ 0.5

Worked example

2 A smoothie is made from 150 ml of milk.
   A smoothie shop has 6 pints of milk.
   Can they make 25 smoothies?

6 pints ≈ 6 × 0.5 = 3 litres
3 litres = 3 × 1000 = 3000 ml
3000 ÷ 150 = 20
No, the shop can only make 20 smoothies.

Work out how much 6 pints of milk is in millilitres. Then work out how many smoothies you can make from that quantity of milk.

Now try this

1 (a) Convert 5 gallons to litres.   (b) Convert 4 litres to pints.
2 Brian needs 5 litres of paint to paint a wall. Paint is sold in 2 litre tins and 500 ml tins.
   Brian doesn't want any paint left over. What combination of tins of paint should he buy?

Temperature

You will usually see temperature measured in degrees Celsius (°C), but you may also see it in degrees Fahrenheit (°F). You need to be able to read temperature scales and work out the differences between temperatures.

Measuring temperature

A thermometer measures temperature. This thermometer shows the temperature in degrees Celsius and degrees Fahrenheit.

The scale on the right shows the temperature in °C. The temperature reading is −10°C.

The scale on the left shows the temperature in °F. The temperature reading is 14°F.

Freezing and boiling points

The freezing temperature of water is 0°C which is 32°F.

The boiling temperature of water is 100°C which is 212°F.

Worked example

1 This thermometer shows the temperature on a winter day.

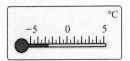

(a) What temperature does the thermometer show?

−2.5°C

(b) The temperature increases by 6°C. What is the temperature now?

3.5°C

Make sure your answer makes sense. If the temperature increases by 6°C, it will be positive.

Worked example

2 The table shows the average monthly temperature in Stockholm during the first six months of the year.

What is the difference in temperature between February and April?

8°C

	°C
Jan	−3
Feb	−3
Mar	0
Apr	5
May	11
Jun	16

Count up to 0, then count on to 5

Now try this

A warehouse freezer must be kept at a temperature of −18°C or below. A health and safety inspector takes the temperature in the freezer with this thermometer.

The thermometer is faulty and the reading is actually 5°C too low. Is the freezer still below the necessary temperature?

47

Money

You need to be able to calculate with money and convert between pounds and pence.

Worked example

Joe's cafe

coffee	£2.25
tea	£1.75
squash	99p
soup	£3.60
bread roll	80p
sandwich	£3.05

1 Ami buys 4 coffees, 2 teas, 4 soups and 5 sandwiches. She also has to pay 10% of the total bill as a service charge. She pays with two £20 notes and a £10 note. How much change should she get?

coffee: 4 × £2.25 = £9

tea: 2 × £1.75 = £3.50

soup: 4 × £3.60 = £14.40

sandwiches: 5 × £3.05 = £15.25

total cost of food: £9 + £3.50 + £14.40 + £15.25 = £42.15

10% of £42.15 = 0.10 × 42.15

$\qquad\qquad\qquad$ = 4.215

$\qquad\qquad\qquad$ = £4.22

Total cost of food and service charge = 42.15 + 4.22

$\qquad\qquad\qquad\qquad\qquad\qquad\qquad\qquad$ = £46.37

£20 + £20 + £10 = £50

$\qquad$ £50 − £46.37 = £3.63

 Subtract the total cost from the amount of money Ami pays.

Worked example

2 A coat costs £35 plus VAT at 20%. What is the total cost?

20% of £35 is $\dfrac{20}{100}$ × £35 = £7

£35 + £7 = £42

VAT

VAT means 'Value Added Tax'. VAT is added to the cost of many things that you buy.

The cost of VAT is 20% of the original price. Calculate this value and add it to the original price.

Now try this

1 Lily is taking her two children to a museum. One of her children is a student and her entry costs £4.62. Her other child's ticket costs £2.84. Lily's adult ticket costs £6.50. Lily pays with a £20 note. How much change does she get?

2 A shop sells baked beans in large tubs or packs of four individual cans. A large tub contains 1 kg and costs £2.50. Each individual can contains 375 g and a pack of four costs £2.65
Which is the better value for money?

Profit and loss

Profit and loss are the differences between the amount earned by selling an item and the amount spent making or buying it. You can calculate profit and loss as an amount of money or as a percentage of the original amount.

Worked example

1 Maria makes beaded bracelets. Each one costs £8.20 to make.
She sells four bracelets for £30
How much profit or loss does Maria make?

profit or loss = £30 − (4 × £8.20)

= −£2.80 so Maria makes a loss of £2.80.

If the cost to make all four bracelets is greater than £30, then Maria makes a loss.

Percentage profit or loss

You can work out profit or loss as a percentage using this formula.

Percentage profit or loss

$$= \frac{\text{amount of profit or loss}}{\text{cost of making or buying}} \times 100$$

Worked example

2 Jo bought a car for £5,000 and sold it for £6,500. Work out the percentage profit.

profit = £6,500 − £5,000 = £1,500

percentage profit = $\frac{1500}{5000}$ × 100 = 30%

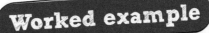

30% profit means that Jo sold the car for 30% more money than she originally spent.

3 Zara makes picture frames for £28 each and sells them for £42 each. Zara aims to make a 55% profit on each picture frame. Does she achieve her aim?

profit = 42 − 28 = £14

percentage profit = $\frac{14}{28}$ × 100 = 50%

She does not achieve her aim.

Now try this

Noel buys and sells antiques. The table shows information about five antiques that Noel bought and sold.

Antique	A	B	C	D	E
bought	£200	£7,800	£4,200	£........	£650
sold	£900	£9,000	£......	£11,200	£575
profit or loss	£700 profit	£.........	£1,500 loss	£500 profit	£........

(a) Copy and complete the table.
(b) Noel wants to make a profit of at least 5%. Has he reached his target? Explain your answer.

Currency conversions

When you go to a different country, you need to know how to convert between different currencies. The two currencies will be in direct proportion.

Worked example

1 Chad is going on holiday to Australia. He finds out that the exchange rate is £1 = $2.03

He changes £560 into Australian dollars.

(a) How many Australian dollars does he receive?

560 × 2.03 = 1136.8 $1,136.80

(b) When he returns, he changes the $121 he didn't spend back to pounds. How many pounds does he receive to the nearest penny?

121 ÷ 2.03 = 59.60591133
             ≈ £59.61

> The two currencies are in direct proportion with one another.

> Multiply the amount in pounds by the exchange rate to find the amount in Australian dollars.

> To change from Australian dollars to pounds, divide by the exchange rate.

> See page 27 for more about direct proportion.

Worked example

2 This graph can be used to convert between euros and pounds.

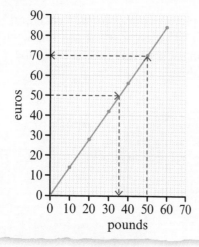

(a) How many euros is £50?

70 euros

(b) How many pounds is 50 euros?

£35.70

> Read up from £50 on the horizontal axis and read across to the vertical axis.

> Read across from 50 euros on the vertical axis and down to the horizontal axis.

Now try this

Natalia is going on holiday to Denmark. She changes £450 into Danish krone (DKK) using this exchange rate:

£1 = 9.72 DKK

(a) How many krone does she receive?

(b) At the end of her holiday, Natalia changes 120 DKK into pounds at the same exchange rate. How many pounds does Natalia receive? Give your answer to the nearest penny.

> Work out 120 ÷ 9.72 and then round to 2 decimal places.

Problem-solving practice

When you are solving problems, you need to:
- ✓ read the question
- ✓ check your answers
- ✓ decide which calculation you are going to use
- ✓ make sure you have answered the question asked.

1 These scales show the weights of two different bags of carrots.

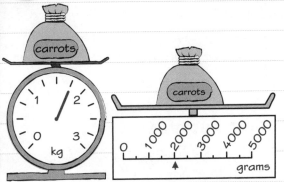

Work out the difference in weight.
Give your answer in kg.

Scales page 41 and Weight page 45

Read the weights on both scales.
Convert them to the same units before completing your calculation.

TOP TIP

Remember to write your answer in kg.

---

2 The mileage chart shows the distances between different towns in miles.

Ashford			
224	Crewe		
270	42	Horwich	
112	192	230	Lymington

Joe drives from Ashford to Horwich. He leaves home at 9 a.m. and travels at an average speed of 60 mph.

He stops on the way for breakfast for 45 minutes.

What time does he arrive in Horwich? Write the time in the 24-hour clock.

12-and 24-hour clock page 35 and Speed page 44

Work out how long it takes Joe to travel from Ashford to Horwich.

Don't forget that Joe stops for breakfast on the way.

TOP TIP

Drawing a timeline might help.

---

3 A shop sells cans of drink in packs of six or eight.

A pack of six costs £3.12
A pack of eight costs £4.08
Which is the better value for money?

Money page 48

Work out the cost of one drink for each pack.

TOP TIP

Remember to answer the question. You must make a decision about which is the better value for money and use your calculations to show your reasons.

Problem-solving practice

 Karl is carrying out a science experiment.

He records the temperature in a freezer with the door open at different times.

Here are his results.

Time	2 p.m.	3 p.m.	4 p.m.	5 p.m.
Temp	−18°C	−2°C	9°C	12°C

Karl says that the temperature rose by 9°C between 2 p.m. and 4 p.m.

Is Karl correct?

Negative numbers page 5 and Temperature page 47

Work out the difference between −18°C and 9°C.

You need to show all your working and state whether Karl is correct or not.

TOP TIP

You can sketch a number line to help with questions about negative numbers.

 Javid is planning a trip for a group of 20 children and 5 adults.

They can go to either the theatre or the zoo.

If they go to the theatre, they will go by train.

If they go to the zoo, they will go by coach.

Javid has this information about the costs.

theatre ticket prices	return train fares
stalls: £22	adults: £11.50
circle: £15	child: £5.75

zoo admission	coach hire
adult: £18	20 seats: £190
child: £12	30 seats: £240
	40 seats: £300

What is the lowest possible total cost of the trip? You must show all your working.

Money page 48

Work out the total cost of each trip.

Remember to choose the cheapest ticket price for the theatre tickets, and write down all your working.

You have to say which trip is the cheapest to complete your answer.

TOP TIP

Plan how you will lay out your answer. You need to show what you are working out at each stage, so you can decide which is the lowest possible total cost.

 Mark bought a bag in Spain. He paid 45 euros for it.

In the UK, the same bag costs £38

The exchange rate was £1 = 1.3 euros.

In which country was the bag cheaper, and by how much? Give your answer in pounds.

Show all your working.

Currency conversions page 50

Convert 45 euros to pounds. You will need to round your answer to 2 decimal places to find the answer in pounds.

Then compare the cost of the bag in pounds. You can then work out the difference.

TOP TIP

Remember to say which country is cheaper.

Symmetry

You need to be able to spot lines of symmetry and rotational symmetry in shapes. If you tile a room with patterned tiles, you may need to make sure the tiles are in a symmetrical pattern.

Lines of symmetry

A line of symmetry is a mirror line.

no lines of symmetry

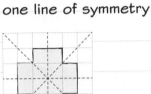

one line of symmetry

two lines of symmetry

four lines of symmetry

Using tracing paper

You are allowed to ask for tracing paper in your test. You can use it to check for lines of symmetry.

If you fold a tracing of a shape in half along a line of symmetry the two halves will match up exactly.

Rotational symmetry

If a shape fits over itself when it is rotated then it has rotational symmetry. The order of rotational symmetry tells you how many times it fits over itself in one full turn.

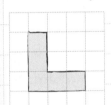

no rotational symmetry

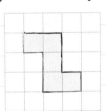

rotational symmetry of order 2

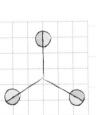

rotational symmetry of order 3

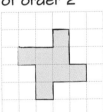

rotational symmetry of order 4

Using tracing paper

You can use tracing paper to check for rotational symmetry.

Trace the shape. Rotate the tracing paper and see how many times the shape fits over itself.

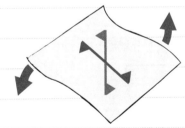

This shape fits over itself twice: once at 180° and once at 360°.

Now try this

(a) Shade four more tiles below to make a set of tiles with exactly four lines of symmetry.

(b) Shade four more tiles to make a set of tiles with rotational symmetry of order 2

Properties of 2D shapes

You need to be able to recognise 2D shapes and identify their properties.

Regular or irregular?

A shape is **regular** if all of its sides and angles are the same size.

A shape is **irregular** if its sides or angles are not all the same size.

regular shapes

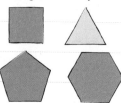

irregular shapes

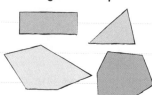

Tessellation

Shapes which **tessellate** can fit together with no gaps.

This diagram shows the tessellation of an irregular hexagon.

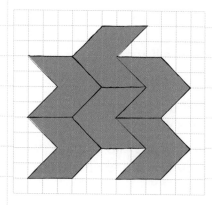

Worked example

On the grid, show how this shape will tessellate. Draw at least six shapes.

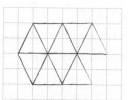

Notice that the triangle has been rotated.

The triangle has not changed its shape or size but it has changed its **orientation**.

Names of 2D shapes

triangle	quadrilateral	pentagon	hexagon	heptagon	octagon
3 sides	4 sides	5 sides	6 sides	7 sides	8 sides

Now try this

Copy and complete the tessellation. Draw at least six more shapes.

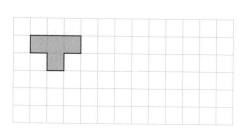

3D shapes and nets

You need to learn the names of common 3D shapes and recognise their nets.

Common 3D shapes

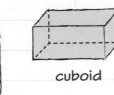
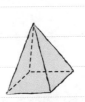

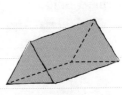

cone   cube   cylinder   cuboid   square-based pyramid   sphere   triangular prism

Faces, edges and vertices

A 3D solid has faces, edges and vertices.

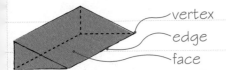

vertex
edge
face

The plural of vertex is vertices.

Prisms

A prism is a 3D shape which has the same cross-section throughout its length.

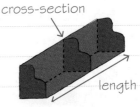

cross-section

length

The cross-section is perpendicular to the length.

Nets

The net of a 3D shape is a 2D shape that folds up to make the 3D solid.

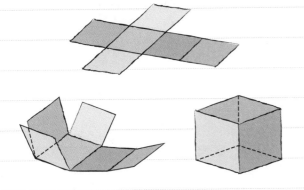

Imagine folding each net along the lines. Only net B makes a solid shape without any overlapping sides.

Worked example

Circle the net that folds to make a cube.

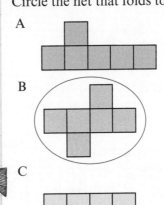

A

B

C

Now try this

Copy and complete the net of this cuboid.

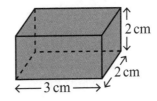

2 cm

2 cm

3 cm

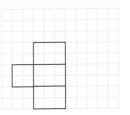

Scale drawings and maps

Scales are used on maps and scale drawings so that you can work out real distances.

Scale drawings

This is a **scale drawing** of the Queen Mary cruise ship.

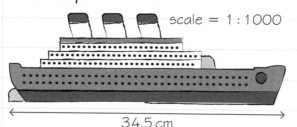

scale = 1 : 1000

34.5 cm

You can use the scale to work out the length of the actual ship.

34.5 × 1000 = 34 500

The ship is 34 500 cm or 345 m long.

Map scales

Map scales can be written in different ways:

- 1 : 25 000
- 1 to 25 000
- 1 cm represents 25 000 cm
- 1 cm represents 250 m
- 4 cm represent 1 km

MAP

SCALE
1 : 25 000

Worked example

The diagram shows a scale drawing of a theme park. The scale is 1 : 3000

(a) What is the real distance between the bumper cars and the cafe in metres?

3000 × 6 cm = 18 000 cm
= 180 m

(b) The roller coaster is 150 m east from the cafe. Mark its position with a cross and label it.

(b) 150 m = 15 000 cm
15 000 ÷ 3000 = 5
Draw the cross 5 cm to the right of the cafe.

(a) Use a ruler to measure the distance from the bumper cars to the cafe.

distance = 6 cm

Work out the real distance using the scale and then convert to metres.

Map	Real
1 cm	3000 cm
6 cm	18 000 cm

×6   ×6

bumper ✗ cars

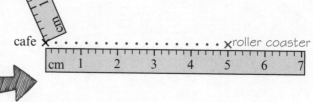

cafe ✗ . . . . ✗ roller coaster

Now try this

This is a scale map of the grounds of a park.

(a) Mischa says the distance between the monument and the lake is less than 250 m. Use the map to show if she is correct or not.

(b) Mischa wants to add the public toilets to the map. The real distance between the monument and the toilets is 400 m. What will be the distance on the map?

lake
✗

monument
✗

scale
1 : 50 000

stepping stones
 ✗

Plans and elevations

3D shapes look different depending on which direction you look at them. If you look at a shape from above, you will see the **plan**. If you look at it from the front, back or a side, you will see an **elevation**.

  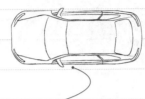 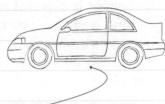

front elevation   plan   side elevation

Worked example

Imagine rotating the shape to work out what it will look like from different angles.

1 This diagram shows a 3D shape.

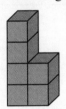

Draw a plan view and front and side elevations of the shape.

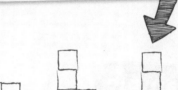

plan   front elevation   side elevation

Worked example

2 Penny wants to work out where to put the table in her living room.
The room is 4 m by 4.5 m.
The table needs a rectangular space 1.5 m by 2 m.
The table must be:

- at least 1 m from the window
- at least 1 m from the sofa
- at least 1.5 m from the door
- at least 1 m from the bookshelf.

Penny draws a plan of the room.
Add the table to the plan.
Remember to use the key.

Key: 1 square = 0.5 m by 0.5 m
——— represents a wall

There are different positions where you can put the table. Try different positions and check that all the conditions are met.

Now try this

This solid is made from centimetre cubes.
On squared paper, draw:
(a) the plan view of the solid
(b) the front elevation of the solid
(c) the side elevation of the solid.

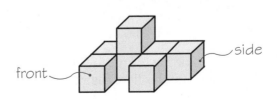

Perimeter and area

Here is a reminder of the difference between perimeter and area.

Perimeter

Perimeter is the distance **around** a shape. You can work out the perimeter of a shape by adding up the lengths of the sides.

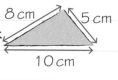

perimeter = 5 cm + 8 cm + 10 cm

$\qquad$ = 23 cm

In your test, you might need to measure a shape to find its perimeter.

Area

Area is the amount of space **inside** a shape. Area is measured in squared units.

You can work out the area of a shape drawn on cm squared paper by counting squares or using a formula.

Golden rule

Always write the units with your answer.

Units of perimeter are mm, cm, m or km.

Units of area are mm^2, cm^2, m^2 or km^2.

Worked example

Claire is decorating a rectangular window with fairy lights.
The window is 1.5 m wide and 1 m tall.
The fairy lights have to go around the window at least twice.
Claire has 8 m of fairy lights.
Does she have enough to decorate the window?

perimeter of window = 1.5 m + 1.5 m + 1 m + 1 m

$\qquad\qquad\qquad$ = 5 m

5 × 2 = 10 m

No, Claire does not have enough fairy lights. She only has 8 m and needs at least 10 m.

> Start by calculating the perimeter of the window.

> The lights have to go around the window at least twice, so double the perimeter of the window to find the required length.

Estimating

You might need to estimate the area of a shape drawn on cm squared paper.

Count 1 cm^2 for every whole square and for every part square that is more than half full. Do not count squares that are less than half full.

Here there are 10 whole squares.
2 squares are less than half full and 4 squares are more than half full.
A good estimate for the area of the whole shape is 14 cm^2.

Now try this

> Don't forget to work out the missing lengths.

Sandeep needs to buy new skirting boards for his living room. He needs to leave a space of 1.5 m for a door. Use this floor plan to work out the length of skirting board he needs to buy in metres.

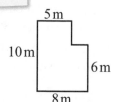

Area of rectangles

Here is a reminder of how to find the area of a rectangle using a formula.

Area of a rectangle

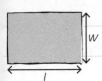

Area = length × width

$A = lw$

Golden rule

☑ Check the lengths are all in the same units before working out the area.

☑ Remember to give units in your answer.

☑ Lengths in cm will give areas in cm².

☑ Lengths in m will give areas in m².

Divide the area of the garden by the area of one piece of turf to work out how many pieces of turf Petra needs.

Worked example

1 Petra is going to lay turf in her garden.

Her garden is rectangular. She draws this sketch of her garden.

42 m

25 m

Each piece of turf is 1 m wide and 3 m long. The turf can be cut and joined together to fill any gaps. How many pieces of turf does Petra need to buy?

area of garden = 42 × 25
          = 1050 m²

area of turf = 1 × 3
         = 3 m²

number of pieces of turf needed = 1050 ÷ 3
                    = 350

Worked example

2 This diagram shows the floor of a rectangular room.

3 m

4 m

Carpet costs £12 per m² and carpet underlay costs £5.99 per m².

How much will it cost to buy enough underlay and carpet for the room?

You need to find the area of the room before you can work out the cost of each item.

$A = l × w$
$A = 5 × 4$
  = 20 m²

cost of underlay
20 × 5.99 = £119.80

cost of carpet
20 × 12 = £240

total cost = £240 + £119.80
       = £359.80

Now try this

Angharad needs to paint a wall in her bedroom.
The wall is 8 m wide and 3 m high.
One tin of paint can cover 10 m².
Each tin of paint costs £8.99
How much does it cost her to paint the wall?

Triangles

There are different types of triangles you need to know.

scalene	isosceles	equilateral	right-angled

All sides are different lengths and all angles are different.

Two sides have equal lengths and two angles are equal.

All sides are the same length and all angles are equal.

One angle is 90°

Area of a triangle

The formula for the area of a triangle is:

$$\text{Area} = \frac{\text{base} \times \text{vertical height}}{2}$$

$$A = \frac{1}{2}bh$$

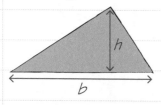

b is the length of the base.

h is the vertical height.

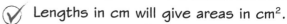

Golden rule

Check the lengths are all in the same units before working out the area.

Remember to give units in your answer.

☑ Lengths in cm will give areas in cm².

☑ Lengths in m will give areas in m².

Worked example

Beth is making bunting out of fabric.

She cuts 22 triangles from a rectangular piece of fabric 2.5 m long and 0.3 m wide.

Work out the area of fabric she has left over.

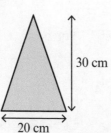

30 cm

20 cm

Don't forget to write the units in your answer.

area of one triangle $= \frac{1}{2}bh$

$\qquad\qquad\qquad = \frac{1}{2} \times 20 \times 30$

$\qquad\qquad\qquad = 300\,\text{cm}^2$

area of 22 triangles $= 6600\,\text{cm}^2$

area of fabric $= 250 \times 30$

$\qquad\qquad\quad = 7500\,\text{cm}^2$

remaining fabric $= 7500 - 6600$

$\qquad\qquad\qquad = 900\,\text{cm}^2$

Now try this

Find the area of this triangle.

12 m

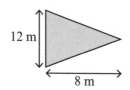

8 m

Circles

You need to know what all of the features of a circle are and how to work out various lengths from others.

Parts of a circle

You need to know these parts of a circle.

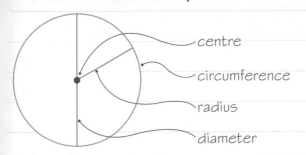

centre

circumference

radius

diameter

Pi

π is the symbol for the Greek letter 'pi'.

π = 3.1415926...

You can round π to **3.142** when using it for calculations, but a scientific calculator will have a button for π.

You may be asked to write your answer in terms of π. Just calculate with the numbers and leave π in your answer.

Circumference

The circumference is the **perimeter** of a circle.
The formula for the circumference of a circle is

C = π × diameter   C = πd

> The radius, r, is half the diameter, d.

Worked example

1 A circle has a radius of 18 cm.
   Work out the circumference of this circle.
   Give your answer to 1 decimal place.

   r = 18 cm
   circumference = 2πr
                 = 2 × 3.142 × 18
                 = 113.1 cm (to 1 d.p.)

Worked example

2 Here is a semi-circular tile. The diameter of the semicircle is 0.4 m. Work out the perimeter of the tile. Give your answer to 2 decimal places.

0.4 m

circumference of whole circle = π × 0.4
                              = 1.25663...

curved edge of tile = 1.25663 ÷ 2
                    = 0.62831...

total perimeter of tile = 0.4 + 0.62831...
                        = 1.03 m (to 2 d.p.)

> For this shape, work out perimeter
> = circumference ÷ 2 + diameter

Now try this

1 Work out the circumference of these circles:
   (a) circle with radius 3 cm
   (b) circle with diameter 7 cm.

2 Josie wants to put ribbon round a circular box. The diameter of the box is 20 cm. She has 60 cm of ribbon. Does she have enough?

Area of a circle

You need to be able to work out the area of a circle or semicircle.

Finding the area

Area = π × radius²

$A = \pi r^2$

You always need to use the **radius** when you are calculating the area.

If you are given the diameter, divide it by 2 to work out the radius.

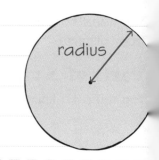

radius

Worked example

The diameter of a semicircle is 15 cm.
Calculate the area of the semicircle.
Give your answer to 2 decimal places.

radius = 15 ÷ 2
     = 7.5 cm

area of whole circle = πr^2
         = π × 7.5²
         = 176.7145... cm²

area of semicircle = area of whole circle ÷ 2
         = 88.36 cm² (to 2 d.p.)

> Be careful: you are given the diameter of the circle but you need the radius to work out the area.

> A semi circle is half a circle, so you have to divide the area of the full circle by 2.

Now try this

A gardener wants to build a path around a flower garden. This diagram shows the flower garden and the path.

The flower garden is in the shape of a circle with diameter 8 m. The path is 2 m wide.
Calculate the area of the path.

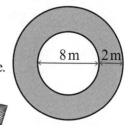

8 m 2 m

> Work out the radius of the flower garden first. Then work out the area of the small circle and subtract it from the area of the large circle.

Properties of compound shapes

You can calculate properties of harder shapes by splitting them into parts.
You might need to draw extra lines on your diagram and add or subtract to find unknown values.

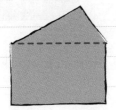
rectangle + triangle

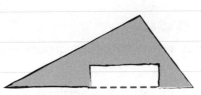
triangle – rectangle

large rectangle – small rectangle

Worked example

(a) Find the area of this shape.

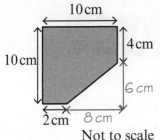
10 cm

10 cm

4 cm

6 cm

2 cm   8 cm

Not to scale

Golden rule
Always work out missing lengths before calculating area or perimeter.

Work out the missing lengths and write them on the diagram.
The diagram is not accurately drawn so you can't use a ruler to measure.
10 – 4 = 6 cm
10 – 2 = 8 cm

area of square = 10 × 10
           = 100 cm²
area of triangle = 6 × 8 ÷ 2
           = 24 cm²
total area of shape = 100 – 24
           = 76 cm²

(b) This diagram shows the floor plan of a shed.

Dan needs to fit a gutter around the full perimeter of the shed.

Calculate how many metres of guttering he will need.

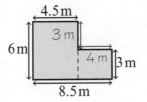
4.5 m

3 m

6 m

4 m   3 m

8.5 m

6 + 4.5 + 3 + 4 + 3 + 8.5
= 29 m

Draw a dotted line to divide the shed into two rectangles.
Work out the missing lengths and write them on the diagram.
8.5 m – 4.5 m = 4 m
6 m – 3 m = 3 m

Now try this

Here is a shape made up of rectangles.
(a) Work out the area of this shape.
(b) Work out the perimeter of this shape.

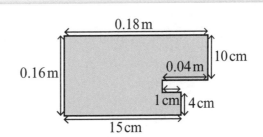
0.18 m

10 cm

0.16 m

0.04 m

1 cm 4 cm

15 cm

Volume

The volume of a 3D shape is the amount of space it takes up. Volume is measured in cubed units such as mm^3, cm^3 or m^3. To work out the volumes of prisms you need to know and use area formulas.

> Look at page 55 for a reminder about prisms.

Finding the volume of a prism

To find the volume of a prism, work out the area of its cross-section and then multiply this by its length.

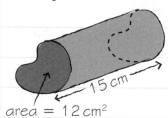

area = $12\,cm^2$, 15 cm

volume = area of cross-section × length

$$= 12 \times 15$$

$$= 180\,cm^3$$

Worked example

1 Work out the volume of this match box.

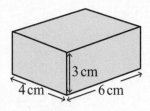

3 cm, 4 cm, 6 cm

volume = area of cross-section × length

$$= (3 \times 6) \times 4$$

$$= 72\,cm^3$$

Don't forget to write the units in your answer.

Worked example

2 Chloe buys a wedge of cheese. Work out the volume of cheese.

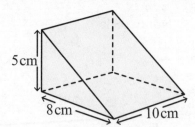

5 cm, 8 cm, 10 cm

volume = area of cross-section × length

$$= (\tfrac{1}{2} \times 8 \times 5) \times 10$$

$$= 200\,cm^3$$

area of a triangle $= \tfrac{1}{2} \times b \times h$

$$= \tfrac{1}{2} \times 8 \times 5$$

Now try this

A cylinder is a type of prism. Start by finding the area of the circular base.

Simon fills this container with water. Calculate the volume of water in the container to 1 decimal place.

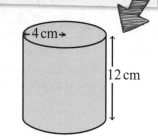

←4 cm→, 12 cm

Problem-solving practice

When you are solving problems, you need to:

- ✓ read the question
- ✓ check your answers
- ✓ decide which calculation you are going to use
- ✓ make sure you have answered the question asked.

1 Rosie is designing a playground. It already has a climbing frame which cannot be moved.

She wants to put in a slide for which she needs a rectangular space 3 m by 1.5 m. The slide must be at least 0.5 m away from the fence. She also wants a rectangular sandpit in a corner of the playground with an area of 6 m². Nothing can be positioned within 1 m of the gate or the climbing frame.

Rosie draws a plan of the playground on a grid.

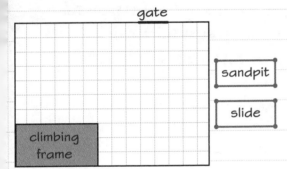

Key

1 square on the grid is 50 cm by 50 cm in the playground.

——————— represents a fence.

Draw and label the slide and the sandpit on the grid.
Remember to use the scale in the key.

Plans and elevations page 57

There are different positions where you can put the sandpit and slide and you may need to turn them so that they fit. Try different positions.

TOP TIP

On the online test the sandpit and slide will be icons. You will need to make sure each icon is the correct size by dragging the dots. You can then drag the icons on the grid.

---

2 Mario is redesigning his garden and wants to lay a patio.

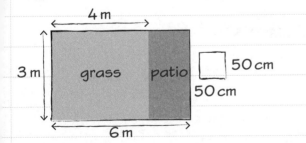

He makes his patio using 50 cm by 50 cm paving slabs. Paving slabs are sold in packs of five.

The cost of a pack is £6

Mario wants to pay as little money as possible for the paving slabs. How much will it cost him to lay the patio?

Area of rectangles page 59

Make sure all values are in the same units.

Mario may need to buy more paving slabs than he actually needs as they are sold in packs.

TOP TIP

In the online test, if you get stuck, you can flag a question to come back to later.

Click the review button so that you can check that question again.

Problem-solving practice

3 The diagram shows a square tile. Four tiles placed together would make a blue circle.

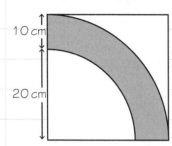

Work out the percentage of the tile that is blue. Give your answer to 1 decimal place.

Area of a circle page 62

Work out the radius of the larger circle.

Find the difference between the area of the larger and smaller quarter-circles.

The percentage of the tile painted is the area painted divided by the total area of the tile multiplied by 100

TOP TIP

Remember to use the π button on your calculator.

4 Jamie uses these tiles to tile a rectangular section of wall with height 0.4 m and length 1.4 m.

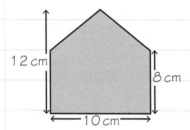

(a) Jamie can cut the tiles in half so that they fit the wall but wants to cut the smallest number possible. What is the minimum number of tiles Jamie needs to cut?

(b) One pack of eight tiles costs £12.50 How much will it cost to tile the wall?

Properties of compound shapes page 63 and Properties of 2D shapes page 54

(a) Draw a diagram to help. Find out if the shape tessellates.

(b) There are different methods you could use to solve this problem.

You could find the total area of the wall and divide this by the area of one tile to find out how many tiles Jamie will need.

TOP TIP

Remember, when calculating with area you need to be working in the same units.

5 This diagram shows an oil drum in the shape of a cylinder of height 84 cm and diameter 58 cm. It is one-quarter full of crude oil.

The formula for the volume of the drum is $V = \pi r^2 h$ where V is the volume, r is the radius of the base and h is the vertical height.

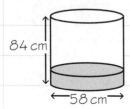

Calculate the volume of oil in the drum. Give your answer in litres, correct to the nearest litre.

Volume page 64

You need to work out the radius to find the area of the circular base.

The cylinder is $\frac{1}{4}$ full so work out $\frac{1}{4}$ of 84 cm to find the height of the oil in the drum.

1 litre = 1000 cm³

TOP TIP

Remember to answer the question asked and give your answer in litres to the nearest litre.

Tables

You need to be able to extract information from tables so that you can solve problems.

Worked example

This table shows information about the cost of booking baggage onto a plane journey.

Luggage	Weight	Cost per bag	
		At the airport	Online
Cabin bag	less than 5 kg	free	free
Hold luggage – maximum of 2 bags allowed	0 – 30 kg	£30	£15
	20 – 30 kg	£45	£32
Excess baggage	per kg over 30 kg	£8	£4

> This row tells you the cost of hold baggage that weighs between 20 kg and 30 kg. The cost is different depending on whether the baggage is booked online or at the airport.

(a) James wants to take one cabin bag weighing 3.5 kg and two hold bags, each weighing between 20 kg and 30 kg.

He wants to book them online.

How much does it cost James?

$2 \times 32 = £64$

(b) Paula has a cabin bag weighing 4.8 kg and two hold bags. One hold bag weighs 18 kg and the other weighs 34 kg.

How much does she have to pay if she pays at the airport?

The cabin bag is free.
The bag weighing 18 kg costs £30
The bag weighing 34 kg costs £45 + (4 × £8) = £77
The total cost is £77 + £30 = £107

> Work out the cost for the bag weighing 34 kg. You need to look at how much more the bag weighs than the 30 kg allowance.
> Then add the cost of the first bag to the cost of the second bag.

Now try this

This table shows information about the hours and pay of two employees one week.

	Employee 1		Employee 2	
	Normal hours	Overtime hours	Normal hours	Overtime hours
Hours worked	25	5	24	8
Pay per hour (£)	£12	normal pay + 50%	£10	double normal pay

Who had earned more money by the end of the week?

Collecting data

A data collection sheet is a useful way of recording data from surveys or experiments.

Worked example

1 Joel is organising activities at his local community centre. He asks young people about their favourite activities. He wants to know their name, their age and whether they prefer sports, crafts, cooking or films. Design a suitable data collection sheet to record this information.

Name	Age	Preferred activity			
		Sports	Crafts	Cooking	Films

Leave space to write each person's name and age.

Write the activities as column headers. You can tick the correct column for each person's choice.

Worked example

2 The manager of a tennis club wants to carry out some research on the age of members and the reasons for their visits. She collects the following information.

Member	Under 16	17–30	31–50	50+	Reason
1	✓				tennis
2			✓		socialise
3			✓		tennis
4		✓			tennis
5			✓		tennis
7		✓			tennis

A two-way table divides data into groups in rows across the table and columns down the table.

The manager decides to divide the members into two groups, 30 years or less and older than 30. Display the information in a two-way table. The table must separate the data by the members' age groups and reasons for visiting the club.

Reason	Age group	
	Under 30	30+
Tennis	3	2
Socialise	0	1

Plan your table before drawing it. There are two age groups and two reasons for visits, so you need two rows and two columns to write the frequencies in.

Now try this

The manager of a cinema finds out the ages of people that watch horror, comedy and romance films. He asks a sample of customers about their film preference and whether they are under 20, between 20 and 39, between 40 and 59, or over 60. Design a suitable table to summarise this information.

Reading bar charts

You can use a bar chart to represent data given in a tally chart or frequency table. You can use more than one bar to show how groups of data compare as long as you include a key.

This dual bar chart shows the number of jeans owned by members of a class.

Dual bar charts have more than one bar for each group. The key tells you what each bar represents.

There is no green bar for 0 pairs of jeans owned so no girls owned 0 pairs of jeans.

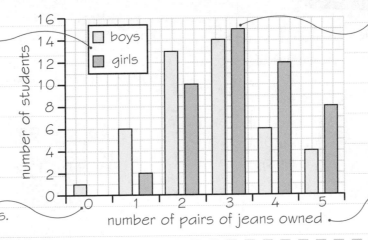

The height of the bar tells you the frequency, in this case 15.

Both axes are clearly labelled.

Worked example

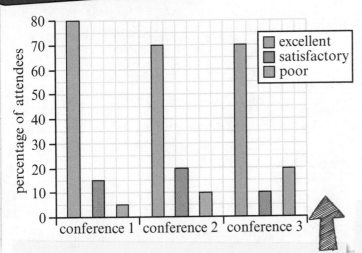

Read the key and the axes carefully to make sure you know which rating and which conference each bar refers to.

This bar chart shows how attendees at three different conferences rated the events.

Which conference was the least successful? Explain your reasoning.

Conference 3 was the least successful. It had the same percentage of excellent feedback as conference 2 but a higher percentage of poor responses than either of the other conferences.

Conference 1 has the highest percentage of 'excellent' ratings and the lowest percentage of 'poor' ratings, so conference 1 was most successful. Compare the bars for conference 2 and conference 3.

Now try this

The bar chart shows the scores of a class in two maths tests. Which test was easier? Use the bar chart to explain your reasoning.

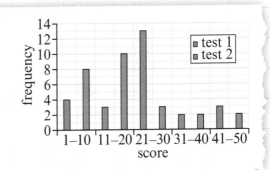

Reading pie charts

A pie chart is a circle divided into slices called sectors. The whole circle represents a set of data. Each sector represents a fraction of the data.

Worked example

A theme park records how many visitors it has each month.

(a) This pie chart shows the number of visitors in 2015

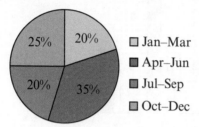

Key:
☐ Jan–Mar
■ Apr–Jun
■ Jul–Sep
☐ Oct–Dec

8000 people visited the theme park in 2015
How many people visited the theme park between April and June?

$$35\% \text{ of } 8000 = \frac{35}{100} \times 8000$$
$$= 2800$$

> Look at the key to find out which sector shows April to June. Then use the percentage shown in that sector to find the number of visitors.

(b) This pie chart shows the number of visitors in 2016. There were 6000 visitors in total.

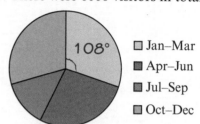

108°

Key:
☐ Jan–Mar
■ Apr–Jun
■ Jul–Sep
☐ Oct–Dec

In 2015, 1600 people visited the theme park between January and March.
Joe said these months were busier in 2016 than in 2015. Is he correct?

The sector for January to March is 108° so this sector represents $\frac{108}{360}$ of the visitors.

$$\frac{108}{360} \text{ of } 6000 = \frac{108}{360} \times 6000$$
$$= 1800$$

Joe is correct. More people visited the theme park between January and March in 2016.

> The angle for the January to March sector is 108°. There are 360° in the full circle so the fraction of the circle this sector represents is $\frac{108}{360}$. Find $\frac{108}{360}$ of the total number of visitors by working out $108 \div 360 \times 6000$

Now try this

The pie charts show the services customers bought at two hair salons in one week. Customers ordered either a cut, a blow dry, colour or highlights.

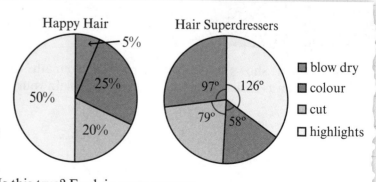

Happy Hair

Hair Superdressers

Key:
■ blow dry
■ colour
☐ cut
☐ highlights

(a) 20 people ordered a blow dry at Happy Hair. How many customers did they have altogether?

(b) Hair Superdressers stated that more than 30% of its customers ordered highlights. Is this true? Explain your answer.

(c) Can you tell which hairdressers had the most customers? Explain your answer.

Reading line graphs

Line graphs show the relationship between two items. This line graph shows average household income for one area from 1980 to 2010

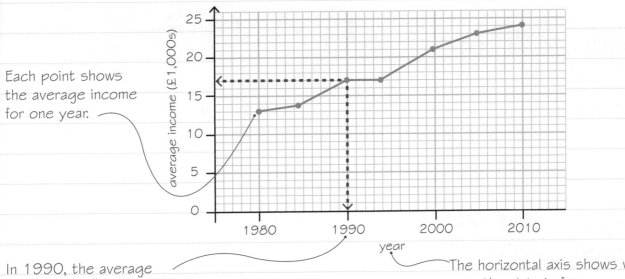

Each point shows the average income for one year.

In 1990, the average income was £17,000

The horizontal axis shows which year the data is for.

Worked example

Sophie's company pays her 50p for each mile she travels. This graph can be used to work out how much her company pays her for travel.

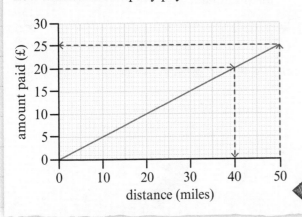

(a) Sophie's company paid her £20.
Work out the distance Sophie travelled.

40 miles

(b) Sophie travels 50 miles. How much will her company pay her?

£25

To find the distance travelled, find the amount paid on the vertical axis, read across to the line and then down to the distance.

To find the amount paid, find the distance on the horizontal axis, read up to the line and then across to the amount paid.

Now try this

This graph shows the cost of buying printed T-shirts from three different companies.
John needs to buy 40 T-shirts and wants to pay the lowest price.
(a) Which shop should he buy the T-shirts from?
(b) How much will they cost?

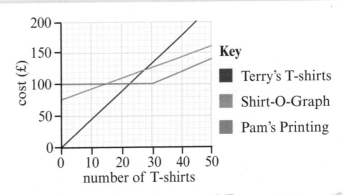

Key

■ Terry's T-shirts
■ Shirt-O-Graph
■ Pam's Printing

Reading scatter graphs

If the points on a scatter graph lie almost on a straight line then the scatter graph shows **correlation**. The closer the points are to a straight line, the stronger the correlation.

Negative correlation

No correlation

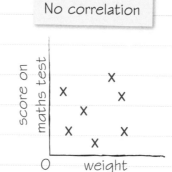

Positive correlation

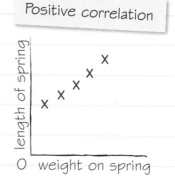

Worked example

This scatter graph shows the daily hours of sunshine and the daily maximum temperature at 10 seaside resorts in England one day last summer.

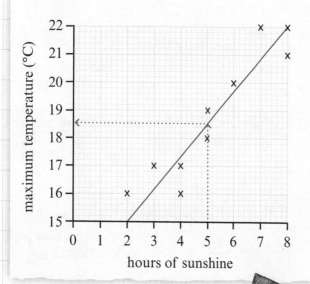

hours of sunshine

The line of best fit has been drawn on in red.

The line of best fit is a straight line that is as close to the points as possible.
The line of best fit does **not** need to pass through (0,0).

(a) Draw a line of best fit to show the relationship between hours of sunshine and the maximum temperature.

(b) Describe the relationship between the number of hours of sunshine and the maximum temperature.

Days with more hours of sunshine tended to have higher maximum temperatures.

(c) Another resort had five hours of sunshine that day.
Use your line of best fit to estimate the maximum temperature at the resort.

18.5 °C

You can use your line of best fit to estimate values that are not plotted. Read up from 5 hours until you reach the line. Read across to the vertical axis.

Now try this

Look at the scatter graph in the worked example above.

(a) Another resort had 6 hours of sunshine. Estimate the maximum temperature at this resort.

(b) On a different day that summer, it had a maximum temperature of 16 °C. Estimate the number of hours of sunshine that day.

Planning a graph or chart

You may be asked to draw a suitable graph or chart to show data you are given. Whatever type of graph or chart you draw, you will need to think about the scale, the axes, and the labels and title.

Choosing a type of graph or chart

Use a line graph to look at the relationship between two sets of data, such as how something changes over time.

Use a bar chart to compare data for different times or places, such as average rainfall in different cities.

Give your graph or chart a title.

Drawing your axes

✓ The vertical axis should start at 0 and go up to at least the largest value.

✓ Decide how much to go up by each time.

✓ You don't need to use all of the space available but try to make the graph as clear as possible.

✓ The data that you measure goes on the vertical axis.

✓ Label both axes to explain what data they show. Include the units.

Worked example

Month	January	February	March	April
Number of projects	12	18	23	21

This table shows the number of building projects worked on by a team over four months.

(a) Which data would you plot on the *x*-axis? Which data will go on the *y*-axis?

Month will go on the x-axis. The number of projects will go on the y-axis.

(b) Your graph paper has 15 horizontal lines. What would be a suitable scale for the *y*-axis?

0 to 24 in jumps of 2

(c) What type of graph would you draw?

Line graph or bar chart

 Sometimes, a bar chart or a line graph would both be suitable. Choose the one you are most comfortable with drawing.

Now try this

Always give your graph a title and label the axes to explain what is shown.

The table shows the amount of money raised by a charity shop through donations and sales over the last five years.

Year	2011	2012	2013	2014	2015
Donations	£9,000	£10,000	£8,000	£11,000	£12,000
Sales	£20,000	£15,000	£21,000	£18,000	£18,000

Draw a suitable graph to show this information.

Drawing bar charts

You can use a bar chart to represent data given in a tally chart or frequency table. Bar charts can include more than one bar for each set of data to represent different categories.

Bar chart features

✓ Bars are the same width.

✓ There is a gap between the bars.

✓ Both axes have labels.

✓ Bars can be drawn horizontally or vertically.

✓ The height (or length) of each bar represents the frequency.

✓ In a dual bar chart two (or more) bars are drawn side by side. They can be used to compare data.

For a reminder about interpreting bar charts, see page 69.

The biggest number is 15, so the scale must go up to at least 15

Make sure the numbers on the scale are equally spaced.

Give your axes labels so it is clear what they are showing.

Worked example

The table shows the number of hot and cold drinks sold daily in a cafe for one week.

	Hot	Cold
Monday	12	10
Tuesday	10	15
Wednesday	9	8
Thursday	15	10
Friday	12	12

Draw a bar chart to show this data.

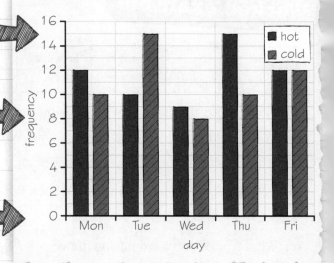

Now try this

The table shows the number of bronze, silver and gold medals won by England and Australia one year in the Commonwealth games.

	England	Australia
Gold	37	74
Silver	59	55
Bronze	46	48

Draw a dual bar chart to show this data.

Think carefully about the increments that your scale will go up in.

Drawing pie charts

You might be given some data and asked to draw a pie chart to represent it. Always use a protractor to measure the angle of each sector.

Worked example

A farm has 40 fruit trees.
The table shows the number of each type of tree.
Draw a pie chart to represent this information.

Type of fruit tree	Number of trees	Angle
Apple	12	$\frac{12}{40} \times 360 = 108°$
Plum	5	$\frac{5}{40} \times 360 = 45°$
Pear	14	$\frac{14}{40} \times 360 = 126°$
Peach	9	$\frac{9}{40} \times 360 = 81°$

Check: $108° + 45° + 126° + 81° = 360°$

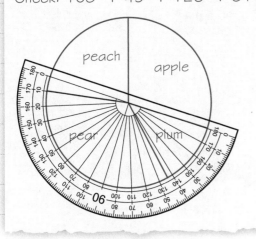

Add an 'Angle' column to the frequency table. 12 out of 40 trees are apple trees, so the angle of the sector for apple trees is $\frac{12}{40}$ of 360° or $\frac{12}{40} \times 360$

Check that your angles add up to 360°

Label each sector of your pie chart with the type of fruit tree.

Draw a circle using compasses and a sharp pencil. Draw a vertical line from the centre to the edge of the circle. Use a protractor to measure and draw the first angle (108°) from this line. Draw each angle carefully in order.

Now try this

This table shows the number of properties an estate agent sold last month.

Property	Number sold
flat	21
studio	9
terraced house	45
semi-detached house	15

Draw a pie chart to represent this data.

Drawing line graphs

Line graphs are a good way of displaying the relationship between two quantities.

Worked example

Peter and John wanted to compare how many sales they made in one day. Every hour, they each recorded the total number of sales they had made so far that day. The table shows the results.

Time	Peter's total sales	John's total sales
09:00	5	10
10:00	7	15
11:00	12	28
12:00	30	30
13:00	32	32
14:00	34	33
15:00	40	35

Use the table to work out the scales for the axes.

The horizontal axis must go from 09:00 to 15:00

The vertical axis must go from 0 to 40

(a) Plot their sales on a line graph.

Plot each point.

At 15:00, Peter had made a total of 40 sales.

Put your finger on 15:00 on the horizontal axis and move up.

Put another finger at 40 on the vertical axis and move across.

Where your two fingers meet, put a mark.

When you have plotted all the points, join them up with a straight line.

Remember to label your axes and add a title to your chart.

(b) Write a statement to compare the number of sales made by Peter and John.

Peter made more sales than John in total. John made more sales before 11:00 and Peter made more sales after 13:00.

Now try this

The table shows the percentage of students who passed an exam each year from 2010 to 2016.

Year	2010	2011	2012	2013	2014	2015	2016
Percentage	58	60	53	55	63	65	73

(a) Draw a line graph to represent this data.
(b) Write a statement to describe how the percentage of passes changes across the years.

Averages

Averages tell you a typical value of a set of data. You need to know the three different types of average – mean, median and mode.

Types of averages

The **mode** is the value which **occurs most often**. There can be no mode or more than one mode for a set of data.

The **median** is the **middle value**. If there are two middle values, the median is halfway between them.

The **mean** is the total of all the numbers divided by how many numbers there are.

Most of the numbers are between 11.5 and 12, so the mean is not a sensible average to use.

Worked example

Alishia times how long in seconds it takes her to run 100 m each day for a week.

	Mon	Tue	Wed	Thu	Fri	Sat	Sun
Time	12	11.8	11.5	11.9	18.2	11.5	11.7

(a) Does the mean or the median make Alishia's average speed seem quicker?

mean: 12 + 11.8 + 11.5 + 11.9 + 18.2 + 11.5 + 11.7 = 88.6

88.6 ÷ 7 ≈ 12.7

median: 11.5 11.5 11.7 <u>11.8</u> 11.9 12 18.2

Mean = 12.7 seconds and median = 11.8 seconds so the median time makes her seem quicker.

(b) Explain why the median is the best average to use.

The data includes one value that is much higher than the others, so the mean is misleading. The mode is not close to the middle of the values.

Choosing the right average

	Pros	Cons
Mean	Uses all the data.	Very small or very large numbers that are not typical of the others affect it.
Median	Not affected by very small or very large values that are not typical.	It can take a long time to work out for a large data set.
Mode	Can be used when the data is described in words, such as colours.	There may be more than one mode, or no mode.

Now try this

A builders' merchant recorded the number of orders they received each week for six weeks.

Week	1	2	3	4	5	6
Number of orders	45	42	41	43	5	46

(a) Work out the mean and median of the number of orders.
(b) Which is the best average to use for this data? Explain your reasoning.
(c) Why is it not possible to find a mode for this data?

77

Range

The range is a value that measures the spread of the data. Make sure you know how to work out the range from a set of numbers, a table or a graph.

Calculating the range

To calculate the range, subtract the lowest value from the highest value.

The tallest bar is for Tuesday, when Anna swam 10 lengths.

The shortest bar is for Friday, when Anna swam 3 lengths.

The range is the greatest number of lengths minus the smallest number of lengths.

Worked example

1 This chart shows the number of lengths Anna swam each day of a week.

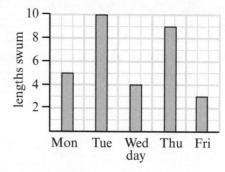

What is the range of the number of lengths she swam?

10 − 3 = 7

Worked example

2 The frequency table shows the number of items bought at a corner shop.

Number of items	Frequency
1	4
2	7
3	5
4	4
5	5

Work out the range of the number of items bought.

5 − 1 = 4

The range is the most items bought minus the fewest items bought.

A common mistake is to subtract the smallest frequency from the largest frequency.

Now try this

This bar chart shows the number of covers two restaurants of the same chain had at two different locations in a city in one week.

Which restaurant had the smallest range of covers?

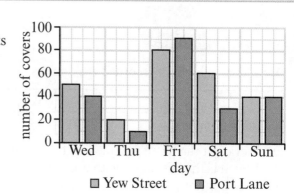

Making a decision

You will need to be able to make decisions based on a set of data. It is often useful to work out averages and the range to compare two sets of data.

Using range and averages

When analysing a set of data to make a decision, you can use the range and averages.

> See pages 77 and 78 for more on how to calculate averages and the range.

If the range is **large**, the data is **more spread out**. If the range is **small**, the data is **less spread out**.

If you wanted to compare how much customers spent in a shop over two days, you could work out the mean and the range.

	Mean	Range
Wednesday	£7.50	£12
Thursday	£8	£3

The amount spent was higher on average on Thursday than on Wednesday.

There was less variation in the amounts that different people spent on Thursday than on Wednesday.

Problem solved!

You need to make a decision based on calculations. The mean and range are useful calculations to use. The mean tells you the average score in the tests. The range tells you how spread out the scores are. Make sure your working is clearly organised to show how you arrived at your decision.

Worked example

This table shows the marks out of 100 that two children received in five subject tests.

	Maths	English	Science	History	ICT
Raheem	74	56	84	59	91
Jenny	69	76	72	73	74

Use the information in the table to decide who performed best overall. Consider whose results were most consistent and whose marks were higher overall.

Raheem
mean: 74 + 56 + 84 + 59 + 91 ÷ 5 = 72.8

range:
91 – 56 = 35

Jenny
mean: 69 + 76 + 72 + 73 + 74 ÷ 5 = 72.8

range:
76 – 69 = 7

Both students had the same mean score but Jenny had a smaller range so her scores were most consistent. Jenny performed best overall.

Now try this

Martina and Ashley want to book a holiday apartment during the ski season in France. The table shows the average monthly snow depth in centimetres in two resorts.

	Dec 15	Jan 16	Feb 16	Mar 16	Apr 16
Val d'Isere	80 cm	74 cm	126 cm	130 cm	122 cm
Alpe d'Huez	81 cm	81 cm	148 cm	124 cm	103 cm

They want to choose the resort that is likely to have the most snow. Which resort should they choose?

79

Probability

Probability is a measure of how likely an event is to happen. You can use fractions, decimals or percentages to describe probabilities.

An event that is **certain** has a probability of 1 or 100%.

An event that is **impossible** has a probability of 0 or 0%.

Worked example

1 On this probability scale, mark the probability that:
- It will rain sometime in Manchester in the next three weeks. (A)
- On a fair dice numbered 1–6, you will throw an odd number. (B)
- You will see an elephant today. (C)

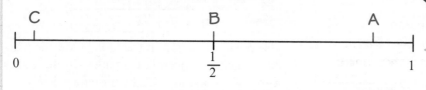

It is very likely that it will rain in Manchester in the next three weeks , so the marker is close to 1

There is an even chance that the dice will land on an odd number, so the marker is at $\frac{1}{2}$

It is unlikely that you will see an elephant today, so the marker is close to 0

Outcomes

All of the possible events that could happen are the outcomes. When you throw a coin, the possible outcomes are that it lands on heads or it lands on tails.

Fair

Fair means that all of the possible outcomes are equally likely. A normal coin is fair because there is a 50% chance it will land on heads and a 50% chance it will land on tails.

Worked example

2 This diagram shows a fair 8-sided spinner. Rory spins it.

(a) What is the probability that the spinner will land on green? $\frac{3}{8}$

(b) What is the probability that the spinner will land on orange? 0

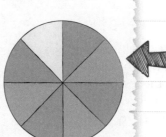

3 out of 8 sections are green so the chance of the spinner landing on green is $\frac{3}{8}$ or 0.375

There are no orange sections so it is impossible the spinner will land on orange. The probability of landing on orange is 0% or 0

Now try this

1 Write an estimation of the probabilities of these events happening:
   (a) The sun will rise tomorrow.
   (b) When you throw a coin it will land tails up.
   (c) It will rain in Scotland in the next week.

2 Isobel said the probability that she will be late for work tomorrow is 7. Is Isobel correct? Explain your reasoning.

Calculating probabilities

You can sometimes calculate probabilities by listing all the outcomes of an event. If each outcome is equally likely to occur, the probabilities will add up to 1. You can write 'the probability of x happening is...' as 'P(x) = ...'

Golden rule

$$probability = \frac{number\ of\ successful\ outcomes}{number\ of\ possible\ outcomes}$$

Worked example

1 Megan has a bag containing six coloured counters. There are two red counters, two blue counters and two yellow counters.

What is the probability she will select:

(a) a blue counter?

$$P(blue) = \frac{1}{3}$$

Two outcomes are successful (blue) out of six possibilities, so P(blue) = $\frac{2}{6}$ or $\frac{1}{3}$

(b) a red or blue counter?

$$P(red\ or\ blue) = \frac{2}{3}$$

Four outcomes are successful (red or blue) out of six possible outcomes, so

$$P(red\ or\ blue) = \frac{4}{6}\ or\ \frac{2}{3}$$

Worked example

2 This diagram shows a fair 8-sided spinner.

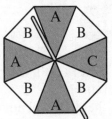

(a) Which letter is the spinner **most** likely to land on?

B

(b) Work out the probability that the spinner lands on the letter A.

$\frac{3}{8}$

There are three letter As, four letter Bs and one letter C. So B is the most likely result.

There are three successful outcomes (A, A or A). There are eight possible outcomes (A, B, C, B, A, B, A, B).

Now try this

1 There are 18 peppermint teabags, 24 breakfast teabags and 12 raspberry teabags in a box. Shani takes one teabag out of the box without looking. Write down the probability that she takes a breakfast teabag.

2 This table shows the flavours of toffees in a bag. Sofia takes a toffee at random from the bag. Write down the probability that she takes a treacle toffee.

Flavour of toffee	fruit and nut	almond	treacle	chocolate
Quantity	3	2	5	2

Start by finding out the total number of toffees.

Adding probabilities

If you are asked to work out the probability that one of two things will happen, you will need to add up the probabilities of each of the things happening separately. The probabilities of all the possible outcomes always add up to 1.

Worked example

1 On a normal, fair dice numbered 1–6, what is the probability of rolling a 1 or a 5?

$P(1 \text{ or } 5) = P(1) + P(5)$

$= \dfrac{1}{6} + \dfrac{1}{6}$

$= \dfrac{2}{6}$

$= \dfrac{1}{3}$

There is a $\dfrac{1}{6}$ chance of rolling a 5 and a $\dfrac{1}{6}$ chance of rolling a 6, so the probability of rolling a 5 or a 6 is $\dfrac{1}{6} + \dfrac{1}{6}$

Golden rule

Remember that probabilities are always between 0 and 1, so your answer should not be greater than 1

You can use the fact that the probabilities of all of the outcomes of an event add up to 1 to work out the probability that something **doesn't** happen.

If you know the probability that something does happen, you can use this formula:

P(event doesn't happen) = 1 – P(event does happen)

Worked example

2 The probability that Dunham FC will win their next football match is 0.65
Work out the probability that they will not win their next football match.

$P(\text{do not win}) = 1 - P(\text{win})$

$= 1 - 0.65$

$= 0.35$

3 The probability that Tim has to work today is $\dfrac{5}{7}$. What is the probability that he does not have to work?

$P(\text{does not work}) = 1 - P(\text{works})$

$= 1 - \dfrac{5}{7}$

$= \dfrac{2}{7}$

Check your answer.

$\dfrac{5}{7} + \dfrac{2}{7} = 1$ ✓

Now try this

1 The probability that Manisha wins a game of chess is 0.73. What is the probability that she doesn't win?

2 The probability that a tram is late is 43%. What is the probability that it is on time?

Combined events

You might need to record all the possible outcomes of two or more events. To show all the possible outcomes, you can list the outcomes or use a sample space diagram.

Worked example

1 Two coins are thrown. What is the probability of both of them landing tails up?

possible outcomes: HH, HT, TH, TT

$P(TT) = \frac{1}{4}$ or 0.25

Write down all the outcomes.

There are four possible outcomes.

There is only one way of getting two tails.

The numerator of the fraction is the number of ways of getting the result (successful outcomes).

The denominator is the number of possible outcomes.

Sample space diagrams

You can draw a sample space diagram to help you find all the possible outcomes of two or more events.

Here are all the possible outcomes when two coins are thrown.

There are four possible outcomes. TH means getting a tail on the first coin and a head on the second coin.

	first coin	
second coin	**H**	**T**
H	HH	TH
T	HT	TT

There are 12 different outcomes. 3 out of 12 include yellow and an even number, so the probability is $\frac{3}{12}$.

Worked example

2 Joseph rolls a 6-sided dice labelled 1, 2, 3, 4, 5 and 6 and a 6-sided spinner coloured red and yellow.

What is the probability that Joseph rolls an even number on the dice and the colour yellow on the spinner?

		Number on the dice					
		1	**2**	**3**	**4**	**5**	**6**
Colour on the spinner	**Red**	R,1	R,2	R,3	R,4	R,5	R,6
	Yellow	Y,1	Y,2	Y,3	Y,4	Y,5	Y,6

P(Even, Yellow) = $\frac{3}{24}$

Now try this

Joyce rolls two dice and adds the results together.

(a) Copy and complete this sample space diagram.

(b) How many possible outcomes are there?

(c) Which total is most likely?

(d) Work out the probability that the total is 10.

1st dice

2nd dice	1	2	3	4	5	6
1						
2						
3						
4						
5						
6						

83

Had a go ☐   Nearly there ☐   Nailed it! ☐

Problem-solving practice

When you are solving problems, you need to:

- ✓ read the question
- ✓ check your answers
- ✓ decide which calculation you are going to use
- ✓ make sure you have answered the question asked.

 The table shows information about the numbers of students absent from Keith's college last week.

	Boys	Girls
Monday	8	10
Tuesday	11	9
Wednesday	12	12
Thursday	14	13
Friday	13	11

Keith wants to compare the data.
Draw a suitable graph or chart.

Drawing bar charts page 74 and Drawing line graphs page 76

In this question you have to choose what type of graph or chart to use. It is best to use a bar chart or a line graph.

TOP TIP

Label both axes correctly.
Draw a key for boys and girls, or make sure it is clear which bars or lines represent boys and which represent girls.

 The times of two 50 m swimmers are recorded below.

Swimmer A time (seconds)	Swimmer B time (seconds)
25.8	25.4
26.8	26.4
26.8	26.2
26.8	25.8
26.5	26.0
25.4	26.2

Who is the better swimmer? Give reasons for your choice.

Making a decision page 79

Calculate the mean and the range for both swimmers.

TOP TIP

You need to make a decision based on calculations.
Make sure your working is clearly organised to show how you arrived at your decision.

Problem-solving practice

3 The bar chart shows the numbers of defective parts that two machines made each month.

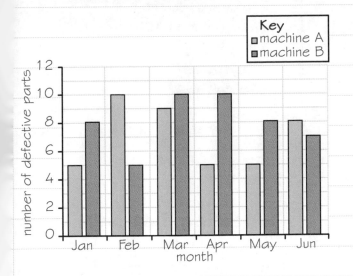

Key
☐ machine A
☐ machine B

(a) Which machine made the most defective parts in total?

(b) In the first six months, both machines produced 500 parts each. The target for each machine is that less than 9% of the parts produced are defective. Did the machines meet their target?

Reading bar charts page 69 and Percentages page 21

(a) Find the total number of defective parts for each machine.

(b) Work out the percentage of parts that were defective by calculating:

$$\frac{\text{number of defective parts}}{500} \times 100$$

TOP TIP

Read the question carefully.

Plan your strategy to solve the problem.

Show your working out clearly.

Draw conclusions based on your calculations.

4 The scatter graph shows the French and German test marks of 15 students.

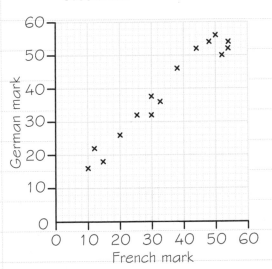

Reading scatter graphs page 72

Draw a line of best fit on the scatter graph first.

TOP TIP

When you are reading information from a graph, you should always give your answer to the nearest small square.

Another student's French mark was 42

Estimate this student's German mark.

Problem-solving practice

 Abi has five cards. Each card has a number written on it.

| 7 | 9 | 3 | 2 | ? |

The mean of the five numbers is 6

One of the numbers is hidden.

Work out the hidden number.

Averages page 77

There are five numbers and the mean is 6, so the sum of the numbers must be 30 because $5 \times 6 = 30$

TOP TIP

Mean × number of data values = sum of data values

 Martin asks a sample of people whether they purchase music online or in a music shop. He asks their age and the number of songs they buy each month.

The table shows the information Martin collects.

Method of purchase	Age	Number of songs
online	under 20	6
online	21–40	8
music shop	over 40	3
online	21–40	5
music shop	under 20	4

Martin wants to sort the information in a summary table. He decides to put the number of songs into two groups – low (fewer than 5) and high (5 or more).

The table should show:

• the type of purchase

• the age group

• whether they buy a low or high number of songs.

Design a table that Martin could use.

Collecting data page 68

Think about the headings in your table. Read the question carefully to check your table shows the necessary information.

TOP TIP

Try writing the data in your table to check that your table works.

 Sofia makes some biscuits.
She makes five shortbread, three chocolate and two ginger biscuits.

She puts the biscuits in a tin.

Sofia's friend takes a biscuit without looking.

What is the probability that the friend chooses a ginger biscuit?

Calculating probabilities page 81

Work out how many biscuits there are altogether.

TOP TIP

Write probabilities as a fraction, decimal or percentage.

Answers

INTRODUCTION

1 Online test preparation

1) Click on the time icon. The time will appear in the bottom right-hand corner of the screen.

2) Zoom in or out or change the colours.

2 Online test tools

1) Because you might still get marks for correct working out even if your final answer is wrong.

2) Practise using the online tools to answer questions.

3 Using the onscreen calculator

Work out each step separately:

(a) Cost of one table:

26 + 2 = £28

Cost of three tables:

3 × 28 = £84

(b) 3 × 50 = £150

150 − 84 = £66

Use a calculator to do all the steps at once:

(a) (26 + 2) × 3 = £84

(b) (3 × 50) − 84 = £66

NUMBER

4 Number and place value

1) (a) forty-three million, three thousand, two hundred and four

(b) 62 500 000

2) (a) 4 hundred   (b) 40 thousand   (c) 40 million

3) 1 502 453   1 452 034   1 425 043   1 402 043

5 Negative numbers

1) −72, −63, −23, 0, 13, 62

2) −22 °C

6 Adding and subtracting

1) £404

2) £1,486

3) 43

7 Multiplication and division

1) 52

2) 52 × 5 = 260 people. So, yes he is correct.

3) £700

8 Brackets

1) (a) 28   (b) 2

2) (32 × 35) + (20 × 12) + (15 × 14) = 1120 + 240 + 210 = £1,570

9 Multiples, factors and primes

1) (a) 16   (b) Any two from 5, 7 or 41

2) 15:42

10 Rounding whole numbers

1) (a) 473 000   (b) 470 000

2) (a) £1,600,000   (b) £2,000,000

3) (a) 376 000 litres   (b) 376 000 litres

11 Fractions

1) $\frac{8}{30}$ or $\frac{4}{15}$

2) $\frac{1}{3}$ kg

12 Simplifying fractions

1) (a) $\frac{8}{14}$ (b) $\frac{3}{6}$

2) $\frac{8}{12}$

3) $\frac{4}{7}$

13 Mixed numbers

1) (a) $\frac{17}{3}$ (b) $2\frac{3}{4}$

2) $\frac{21}{5}$

14 Fractions of amounts

1) $\frac{2}{3}$ of £66 is smaller (£44 compared to £51)

2) £1,200

15 Decimals

1) (a) 8.7   (b) 42.34   (c) 1.06

2) (a) 6 thousandths   (b) 6 tenths

3) 9.0912 litres, 9.192 litres, 9.219 litres, 9.29 litres, 9.921 litres

16 Decimal calculations

1) 46.26 m

2) Nav spent 11p more than Jenny.

17 Rounding decimals

1) (a) 9   (b) 88   (c) 12

2) (a) 1 decimal place: 4.3   2 decimal places: 4.28

(b) 1 decimal place: 0.5   2 decimal places: 0.51

(c) 1 decimal place: 2.1   2 decimal places: 2.10

18 Estimation

1) (a) 900 − 30 = 870

(b) 50 × 10 = 500

(c) 40 ÷ 2 = 20

2) £1,700

19 Checking your answer

1) 800 × 3 − 1000 = 1400

This estimate is a lot lower than 6095 so he is probably incorrect.

2) (a) 2662 − 1239 = 1423, so this is correct

(b) 1335 − 39 = 1296, so this is incorrect

(c) 1590 ÷ 31 = 51.3, so this is incorrect

(d) 436 × 23 = 10028, so this is correct

Answers

20 Fractions and decimals

1) **(a)** 0.8   **(b)** 1.35   **(c)** 1.2   **(d)** 2.75

2) 0.4 kg $\frac{7}{16}$ kg $\frac{5}{8}$ kg   0.75 kg

3) 0.85 kg

21 Percentages

1) $\frac{32}{40} \times 100 = 80\%$

    Yes, she passed the test.

2) 25% of the workers did not work overtime.

3) 934 – 911 = 23 faulty products

    $\frac{23}{934} \times 100 = 2.5\%$ (to 1 decimal place)

    Yes, the company's claim is correct.

22 Percentage calculations

1) £1,278, £852, £426, £284

2) 550

23 Fractions, decimals and percentages

1) 92.3% of customers rated service as excellent in July, so June had the higher percentage of excellent responses.

2) 0.356, $\frac{3}{5}$, 62%

3) Cary wins 104 counters.

24 Percentage change

1) £40.96

2) £7,678.80

25 Ratio

1) **(a)** 3   **(b)** 45

2) 45 : 75 = 3 : 5

3) $\frac{4}{7}$

26 Ratio problems

1) **(a)** 84   **(b)** 140

2) £3,200

3) 162

27 Proportion

1) **(a)** £174.75   **(b)** £419.40

2) £6.72

28 Scaling with ratio

1) 640 g

2) 80.5 g

3) offer A: 4.32 ÷ 12 = £0.36

    offer B: 6.30 ÷ 18 = £0.35

    Offer B is better value for money as the cost of each packet is less.

29 Formulas

(a) £365

(b) Yes because the cost for six days is £493

30 Writing formulas

1) perimeter = 8 × side length of tile

2) total wage (£) = 10 × number of hours + amount of tips

3) 7 spoonfuls

31 Formula problems

1) **(a)** £180

    (b) 21 sales

2) **(a)** p = £12,000 – £2,500 = £9,500

    (b) t = £48,000 + £30,000 = £78,000

32 Problem-solving practice

1) 2 × 6.99 = 13.98

    25 – 13.98 = 11.02

    11.02 ÷ 0.79 = 13.949…

    Aaron can afford to buy 13 songs.

2) <u>Cost of TVs</u>

    80 × 200 = £16,000

    <u>Sales</u>

    Number of TVs sold at £300 each: $\frac{2}{5} \times 80 = 32$

    32 × 300 = £9,600

    Number of TVs sold at £250 each: 25% of 80 = 0.25 × 80 = 20

    20 × 250 = £5,000

    Number of remaining TVs sold at £200: 80 – 32 – 20 = 28

    28 × £200 = £5,600

    <u>Total sales</u>

    9600 + 5000 + 5600 = £20,200

    <u>Total profit</u>

    20 200 – 16 000 = £4,200

    Claire's total amount of profit is £4,200.

3) **(a)** 1.2 × 1800 = 2160

       0.85 × 2160 = 1836

    (b) $\frac{36}{1800} \times 100 = 2\%$

33 Problem-solving practice

4) 3 ÷ 8 × 100 = 37.5%

    45% + 37.5% = 82.5%

    100 – 82.5 = 17.5%

5) 120 ÷ 80 = 1.5

    1.5 × 240 = 360 g

6) **(a)** charge (£) = 25 × number of hours + 50

    (b) charge = 25 × 3 + 50

             = 75 + 50

             = £125

    (c) 5 hours

TIME

34 Units of time

1) Tuesday 2 June

2) 4 hours and 45 minutes (or 4.75 hours)

35 12-hour and 24-hour clock

1)

12-hour	3.12 a.m.	7.50 p.m.	11.30 p.m.	10.15 p.m.
24-hour	03:12	19:50	23:30	22:15

2) 14:35

36 Timetables

(a) 12:24   **(b)** 11:36

37 Creating a time plan

There is more than one correct answer, such as:

Activity	Time of day	Length of activity	Cost
Adventure rides	morning	1.5 hours	£65
Arts and crafts	morning	1 hour	£30
Wildlife show	afternoon	2 hours	£48
Treasure hunt	afternoon	45 mins	£46

38 Problem-solving practice

1) 14:45 2) 08:48

39 Problem-solving practice

3) There is more than one correct answer, such as:

Time	Event
11:00	talk by author
12:30	crafts
13:00	group discussion
13:45	creative writing workshop
15:00	end of day

4) 12:15

5) (a) 09:30 (b) 9 hours

MEASURES

40 Units

1) kilograms or stones (or tons)

2) litres or gallons

3) No, because 7 feet is just a bit more than the average height of an adult man. The height of a double-decker bus must at least be tall enough for two adult men to stand, i.e. one on each level of the bus.

4) Approximately 15 mm (or 1.5 cm) or $\frac{1}{2}$ inch

41 Scales

25 g

42 Routes

1) 196.875 miles

2) Barcelona to Huesca, Huesca to Zaragoza, Zaragoza to Madrid, Madrid to Barcelona

1285 km

43 Length

117 miles = 187.2 km

44 Speed

3 hours and 15 minutes

45 Weight

1) (a) 0.5 stone (b) 200 ounces

2) 4 + 12 + 11 = 27 pounds

46 Capacity

1) (a) 22.5 litres (b) 8 pints

2) He should buy two 2 litre tins and two 500 ml tins.

47 Temperature

The temperature should actually read −19.5 °C so it is still below the necessary temperature.

48 Money

1) £6.04

2) The pack of four cans is better value for money.

49 Profit and loss

(a)

Antique	A	B	C	D	E
bought	£200	£7,800	£4,200	£10,700	£650
sold	£900	£9,000	£2,700	£11,200	£575
profit or loss	£700 profit	£1,200 profit	£1,500 loss	£500 profit	£75 loss

(b) No, because $\frac{825}{23,550} \times 100 = 3.5\%$

50 Currency conversions

(a) 4,374 DKK

(b) £12.35

51 Problem-solving practice

1) 2 kg − 1.75 kg = 0.25 kg

2) 270 ÷ 60 = 4.5 hours or 4 hours and 30 mins

With the 45 mins stop for breakfast the total journey time will be 5 hours and 15 mins

Joe will arrive at 14:15

3) six-pack: price of one drink = £3.12 ÷ 6 = £0.52

eight-pack: price of one drink = £4.08 ÷ 8 = £0.51

The eight-pack is better value for money.

52 Problem-solving practice

4) No, Karl is not correct. The temperature rose by 27 °C.

5) Lowest cost for theatre trip: £15 × 25 + £11.50 × 5 + £5.75 × 20 = £547.50

Lowest cost for zoo trip: £240 + £18 × 5 + £12 × 20 = £570

The lowest possible total cost of the trip is £547.50 to go to the theatre with circle tickets.

6) 45 euros = 45 ÷ 1.3 = £34.62

£38 − £34.62 = £3.38

The bag is cheaper in Spain by £3.38

SHAPE AND SPACE

53 Symmetry

(a)

(b)

Answers

54 Properties of 2D shapes

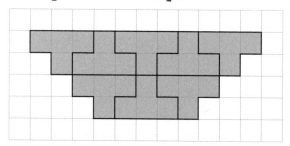

55 3D shapes and nets

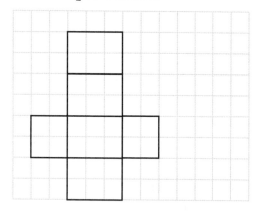

56 Scale drawings and maps

(a) Mischa is incorrect. 50 000 × 4 cm = 200 000 cm or 2000 m, which is more than 250 m

(b) 0.8 cm

57 Plans and elevations

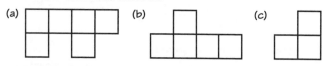

(a) (b) (c)

58 Perimeter and area

34.5 m

59 Area of rectangles

£26.97

60 Triangles

48 m²

61 Circles

1) (a) 18.8 cm   (b) 22.0 cm

2) The circumference of the box = π × 20 = 62.8 cm
   So Josie does not have enough ribbon.

62 Area of a circle

Radius of flower garden = 4 m
Area of flower garden = 50.265 m²
Radius of flower garden and path = 6 m
Area of flower garden and path = 113.097 m²
Area of path = 113.097 – 50.265 = 62.8 m²

63 Properties of compound shapes

(a) 268 cm²   (b) 70 cm

64 Volume

603.2 cm³

65 Problem-solving practice

1) There is more than one correct answer, such as:

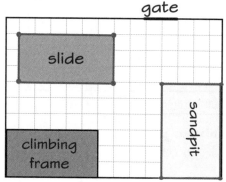

gate

slide

climbing frame

sandpit

Key
1 square on the grid is 50 cm by 50 cm in the playground.

——————————— represents a fence.

2) Mario needs five packs of paving slabs which will cost him £30

66 Problem-solving practice

3) area of larger circle = π (30² ÷4) = 706.8583
   area of smaller circle = π (20² ÷4) = 314.1593
   blue area = 706.8583 – 314.1593 = 392.6991
   area of square = 30 × 30 = 900 cm²
   percentage blue = $\frac{392.699}{900}$ × 100 = 43.6332 = 43.6%

4) (a) The tiles tessellate but to complete the rectangular piece of wall, Jamie must cut two tiles.

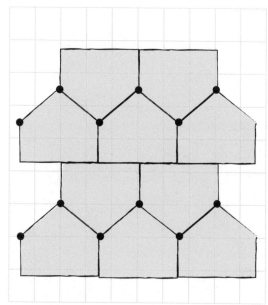

(b) area of the wall = 40 × 140 = 5600 cm²
    area of one tile = 100 cm²
    5600 ÷ 100 = 56 tiles

or:

    number of tiles that can fit across the wall = 140 ÷ 10 = 14
    number of tiles that can fit up = 4 (from diagram)
    number of tiles needed = 14 × 4 = 56 tiles
    56 ÷ 8 = 7
    Jamie needs seven packs of tiles which will cost £87.50

5) Volume of oil in the drum = π 29² ×(84 ÷4) = 55483.7 cm³

The volume of oil in the drum is 55 litres.

HANDLING DATA

67 Tables

Employee 2 earned the most money.

68 Collecting data

There is more than one correct answer, such as:

Age	Preferred film genre		
	Horror	Comedy	Romance
under 20			
20–39			
40–59			
60+			

69 Reading bar charts

Students typically scored higher marks in test 1, so test 1 was easier.

For instance, 18 students scored more than 20 marks in test 1 whilst only 7 students scored more than 20 marks in test 2.

70 Reading pie charts

(a) 400

(b) Yes. The sector for highlights is 126 degrees, so it represents 35% of customers.

(c) You cannot tell because the pie chart tells you the proportion of customers that ordered services not the actual number of people who ordered services. .

71 Reading line graphs

(a) Pam's printing   **(b)** £120

72 Reading scatter graphs

(a) Accept answers between 19.5 °C and 19.8 °C.

(b) Accept answers between 2.8 hours and 3 hours.

73 Planning a graph or chart

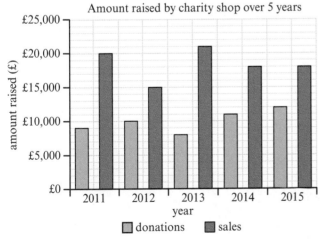

or

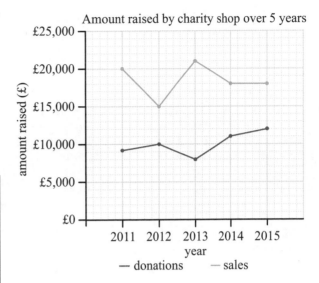

74 Drawing bar charts

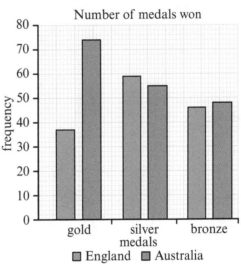

75 Drawing pie charts

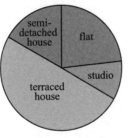

flat = 84°, studio = 36°, terraced house = 180°, semi-detached house = 60°

76 Drawing line graphs

(a)

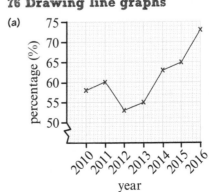

Answers

(b) The percentage of passes increased slightly between 2010 and 2011 and then dropped in 2012. It then continued to rise until 2016.

77 Averages

(a) mean: 222 ÷ 6 = 37; median: 42.5

(b) Median is the best average to use as it ignores the '6' which is not typical of the rest of the data set. The mode is not a good average as it is the highest number. The mean is not a good average as it is affected by the value '6'.

(c) It is impossible to find a mode because there is no value that occurs more often than the others.

78 Range

Yew Street range: 80 − 20 = 60 covers

Port Lane range: 90 − 10 = 80 covers

Yew Street had the smallest range of covers.

79 Making a decision

Val d'Isere

mean: 532 ÷ 5 = 106.4 cm; range: 130 − 74 = 56 cm

Alpe d'Huez

mean: 537 ÷ 5 = 107.4 cm; range: 148 − 81 = 67 cm

Accept any valid answer based on correct analysis of the data. For example:

Alpe d'Huez as it has a larger average snow depth or

Val d'Isere as, although it has a slightly smaller average snow depth than Alpe d'Huez, the range in snow depth is smaller.

80 Probability

1) (a) 1 or 100%   (b) 0.5, $\frac{1}{2}$ or 50%

(c) Answers around 0.6, $\frac{3}{5}$ or 60%

2) She is wrong because probabilities are numbers between 0 and 1 or percentages or fractions.

81 Calculating probabilities

1) $\frac{4}{9}$

2) $\frac{5}{12}$

82 Adding probabilities

1) 0.27

2) 57%

83 Combined events

(a)

		1st dice					
		1	2	3	4	5	6
2nd dice	1	2	3	4	5	6	7
	2	3	4	5	6	7	8
	3	4	5	6	7	8	9
	4	5	6	7	8	9	10
	5	6	7	8	9	10	11
	6	7	8	9	10	11	12

(b) 36   (c) 7   (d) $\frac{3}{36}$ or $\frac{1}{12}$

84 Problem-solving practice

1)

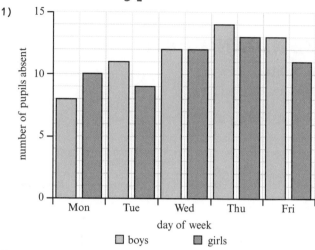

2) swimmer A

mean = 26.35 seconds; range = 1.4 seconds

swimmer B

mean = 26.0 seconds; range = 1.0 seconds

Swimmer B is a better swimmer than swimmer A. They have a smaller average time and their times are less spread out.

85 Problem-solving practice

3) (a) machine A: 42   machine B: 48

Machine B had more defective parts.

(b) machine A: $\frac{42}{500} \times 100 = 8.4\%$ defective

machine B: $\frac{48}{500} \times 100 = 9.6\%$ defective

Machine A met the target but machine B didn't.

4) Answers between 45 and 50 are acceptable depending on the line of best fit drawn.

86 Problem-solving practice

5) 9

6)

	Age					
	Under 20		21–40		Over 40	
Number of songs	low	high	low	high	low	high
Online						
Music shop						

7) $\frac{1}{5}$ or 0.2 or 20%

Notes

Published by Pearson Education Limited, 80 Strand, London, WC2R 0RL.

www.pearsonschoolsandfecolleges.co.uk

Copies of official specifications for all Edexcel qualifications may be found on the website: www.edexcel.com

Text © Pearson Education Limited 2016
Edited, typeset and produced by Elektra Media Ltd
Original illustrations © Pearson Education Limited 2016
Illustrated by Elektra Media Ltd
Cover illustration by Miriam Sturdee

The right of Sharon Bolger to be identified as author of this work has been asserted by her in accordance with the Copyright, Designs and Patents Act 1988.

First published 2016

19 18 17 16
10 9 8 7 6 5 4 3 2 1

British Library Cataloguing in Publication Data
A catalogue record for this book is available from the British Library

ISBN 978 1 292 14570 9

Printed in Italy by Lego S.p.A.